BOSTON TOWN

BOSTON TOWN

BY

HORACE E. SCUDDER

AUTHOR OF THE BODLEY BOOKS

WITH MANY ILLUSTRATIONS ON WOOD

" See, saw, sacradown!
  Which is the way to Boston Town?
  One foot up, the other foot down,
  That is the way to Boston Town."

BOSTON AND NEW YORK
HOUGHTON MIFFLIN COMPANY
The Riverside Press Cambridge

CONTENTS.

———•———

LIST OF ILLUSTRATIONS.

———◆———

viii   *LIST OF ILLUSTRATIONS.*

BOSTON TOWN.

CHAPTER I.

GRANDFATHER'S GRANDFATHER.

WHEN Mr. Benjamin Callender came down to breakfast at his house in Mount Vernon Street, Boston, at half after seven o'clock on the morning of Thursday, November 11, 1880, he found his two grandsons, Benjy and Jeffries, at work at their Latin grammars, snatching a few moments, while waiting for the rest of the family, to freshen their recollection of the morning lesson, which they had been studying over night. They were Latin school boys, as their father had been before them, and their Grandfather Callender. Nay, his father and grandfather had been Latin school boys before him, and his father's grandfather, who died before he was born, was in the Latin school from 1680 to 1683; while his grandfather's grandfather was a member of the very first class of the school when it was established in 1635. The boys gave him a good-morning.

" How was the dinner, grandfather ? " asked Benjy.

" Were you an old boy ? " asked Jeff.

" I was not the oldest. There were two or three older. Yes, the dinner was a good one."

" Did you make a speech ? "

" Tut, tut ; you should n't ask too many questions, Jeff. What should your old grandfather have to say ? "

" Oh, I know you made a speech, then. I wish I had gone to school with you, grandpa. We 'd have had great fun. Mother," said Jeff, as a lady entered the room, " grandfather made a speech at the Latin School Dinner last night. I know he did, and I 'm sure it 's in the paper. I 'm going to see what he said." But grandfather held the morning paper high over his head, out of the boy's reach.

" Come, it 's time for all my boys to sit down at the breakfast table," said Jeff's mother. " You must set your younger brothers a good example, papa. Tell us about your dinner at the Latin School Association last night."

" Oh, there 's nothing to tell. We dined as usual on the ruins of the old Latin school. Benjy, Jeff, *Deponite libros.*"

" What do you mean ? "

" Did you not know that Parker's stands about where the school building was before the school was moved to Bedford Street ? To be sure ; that 's the reason it 's called School Street. I went to school there when I was a boy, and so did your father; for it was not moved till 1844. Master Bigelow and Master Gould were there in my day, and Master Hunt before them. Benjy, Jeff, did n't you hear me, — *Deponite libros*, I say."

"We have n't got as far as that," said Benjy, who was still conning his grammar at the table.

Cheever Latin School in School Street.

"Go to the Latin school, and don't know what that means! Why, what does your teacher say, when school's over and you lay aside your books?"

"Why, he says, 'Boys, put your books away;' and then we all clatter the desk covers."

"You might as well be at an English school. We used Latin, when I was at the Latin school, and it did n't take long to learn what *Deponite libros* meant.

I recollect very well hearing old Mayor Otis tell how
he was on his way to school, on the morning of April
19, 1775, when he found a company of Percy's soldiers across the head of the street, near King's
Chapel. They were getting ready to go to Lexington, and he could n't get by, so he turned back and
went down Court Street, through Washington, and

Master Lovell

so up School Street.
Just as he entered the
school-room, where all
the boys were, he
heard Master Lovell
dismiss them : ' Boys,
war 's begun, and
school 's done. *Depo-
nite libros ;* ' and they
did lay their books by,
and did n't come back
to school till after the
British had left Bos-
ton, when the siege
was raised.   There
were   two   Lovells.
John, the father, was a loyalist, and went off with
the British because he wanted to ; his son James was
a patriot, and went off to Halifax with them because
he did n't want to."

" We don't call them masters now," said Jeff.

" It 's a good name, for all that. But then the

name does n't matter so much, if you have a real
master. Now Master Bigelow was ruled by the boys,
but it was a different thing when Master Gould came.
I remember that first day. The committee had in-
troduced Master Gould to the boys and left the room.
We all began to buzz about him, when he turned
short round and lifted a finger to tell us to keep
silence. It was n't so very big a finger, but the look
that went with it there was no mistaking. Oh, he
was a born master, and he was a good teacher, too.
He made a great deal of the speaking Saturday morn-
ings. You have that now, have n't you, boys?"

"Oh yes, sir."

"Well, mind you attend to it.

> "'How sleep the brave who sink to rest
> By all their country's wishes blest!
> When Spring, with dewy fingers cold,
> Returns to deck their hallowed mould,
> She there shall dress a sweeter sod
> Than Fancy's feet have ever trod.'

That's what I used to speak. That was the first
piece I learned at the Latin school."

"Did your legs tremble, grandfather? Mine always do, and I'm not a bit afraid either. I wonder
what makes them?"

"Almost all boys' legs tremble, Benjy. It's the
way the legs are made. Don't you mind it. If
your head's all right, you'll soon forget all about
your legs, and they will stop trembling."

"My legs had all they wanted to do," said Jeff,

" when I marched in the procession on the seventeenth of September; and I did n't see much of anything either.   I thought it would be great fun to march, but I forgot I could n't march and see the show too; and I shan't be here next time Boston celebrates her two hundred and fiftieth."

" Of course you won't," said Benjy, with some scorn.   " How do you suppose there can be two two hundred and fiftieths!   But when we 're fifty years older, Jeff, we 'll ride in carriages and have a banner with 'Latin School Boys in 1880' on it."

" Not I.   I 'm going to be at a window to see my grandchildren march, and see the grand chancellor of the universal world.   You saw him — did n't you, mother ? "

" Something of the sort," she laughed.   "I saw a man dressed to look unlike anybody else, who pranced about as if he owned the town."

" It was a great procession," said Grandfather Callender ; " and Boston never looked handsomer. I was glad Governor Winthrop saw it from Scollay Square, and I wish Sam Adams could have seen it on Washington Street."

" I remember such processions of trades when I was a little girl," said the boys' mother.   " I liked nothing better than to scramble for the crackers that they baked in carts and threw into the streets.   That old printing-press of Franklin's has figured in every procession that I can remember."

" Your grandfather, Sally, used to tell me about Washington's visit to Boston in 1789, when the school children were drawn up in a file where the general was to pass. They all had long quills in their hands, such as they used then for writing ; and when Washington went by, they all rolled the quills between their palms. It was a queer kind of salute. I never understood how they happened to do it. Everybody laughed, though I don't believe Washington did. There was a triumphal arch stretched across Washington Street, from the old State House, which was decorated with flags, flowers, and ever-greens, and a chorus was stationed there on top of the arch, which began to sing loudly as soon as Washington came near, and until he had passed through the arch. I think that was better than a band of music. Next time your mother sends you to Pierce's grocery store on an errand, do you stand by Winthrop's statue, and look up at the face of the building, and tell me what you see."

" Oh, I know," said Jeff ; " I 've seen it. It 's a tablet in the wall, where it says, ' Occupied by Washington in 1789. I never understood what it was. It was a fort — was n't it ? "

" A fort ? Oh no ; it was only Joseph Ingersoll's boarding-house, where Washington stayed."

" I should n't think General Washington would have stayed at a boarding-house," said Benjy.

" It was quite the only good public house that he

could stay at.   The taverns were not so comforta-
ble."

"Why did n't he stay at the governor's ?   I should
think the governor ought to have invited him."

John Hancock

"The governor was a vain man.   He was the John
Hancock who writ his name so large at the head of
the Declaration of Independence, and he had a no-

tion that as governor of Massachusetts he was a kind of independent sovereign, and that it was the duty of the President of the United States first to call upon him. He did not dare say this outright, but he made a great dinner and invited the President to it, excusing himself from first calling to pay his respects on the ground that he was ill at home. Washington declined the invitation, and intimated that a man who was well enough to give a dinner party was well enough to call on his guest. So Hancock, who saw his mistake, sent word that he should call the next day at any hazard."

" Well, was he really sick, grandpa ? "

" No, but he was a high liver, and he suffered from the gout so that he sometimes had to be carried about, and in that fashion he was taken to see Washington. I presume he made himself look as helpless as possible."

" You have dined at Hancock's house — have n't you, grandfather ? "

" Yes, Benjy. I am sorry you never could have seen the house. You pass the place every day when you go to school, but there is nothing to remind you of the old stone mansion which stood back from the street near the top of the hill."

" Did you ever see Hancock ? "

" No, he died in 1793, — four years after Washington was here. I have often heard my father speak of his funeral. Father was a little over thirty

2

years old then, and marched in the procession, as one
of the militia.   It was the greatest funeral ever had
in Boston, they said.   People went afoot then, as
they ought to go, and carried the bier instead of
shoving it into a wagon and getting into carriages

The Hancock House

themselves.   You can see his tomb now in the old
Granary Burying Ground on Tremont Street."
    "Somehow," said Jeff, "it always seems as if you
must have seen all these people, grandfather, you 're
so old, and know all about them."   Grandfather
laughed.
    "Well, I 'm not so very old, but I can remember

my grandfather, who was ninety-six when he died. I was eight years old then, — a little younger than you, Benjy, — and grandfather used to tell me stories. He was born in 1717, and he could remember his grandfather who was born in 1630, the very year the town of Boston was founded ; for we have been a long-lived family. My grandfather's grandfather was eighty-seven years old when grandfather was born, and he lived to be ninety-seven ; so you see I have heard my grandfather tell stories which he heard from his grandfather. Think of it, Jeff and Benjy, his grandfather was a friend of Winthrop and Endicott, and Bradford of Plymouth ; and my grandfather knew Judge Sewall and Cotton Mather and Franklin ; and my father knew Sam Adams and Copley, and Knox, and had seen Washington " —

" Yes," broke in his daughter, " and you knew John Adams and John Quincy Adams and Webster."

" To be sure, and so it does almost seem as if I ought to be as old as Boston, for I can remember, by my grandfather's help, back to the founding of it."

" Hurra ! " said Jeff. " Grandpa, you ought to have marched in the procession. You ought to be a procession all by yourself."

" Come, come ; don't make fun of your old grandfather. I'm not so very old. I didn't go to sleep in the last century and wake up in this, as some of my friends who are five years older boast of doing."

"Any way," said Benjy, "I don't believe anything ever happened in Boston that grandfather has n't heard of."

"That's because I've always lived here, Benjy, and have had such very old grandfathers. But Boston is a much bigger place than when I was a boy. Why, I remember" —

"My dear father, if you don't eat your breakfast the boys never will; and they will be late at school. You must start your grandfather in the evening, boys, and then you won't stop his eating."

"But we should stop his nap, mother. He always takes a nap after tea. Which would you rather do, grandfather, eat or sleep?"

"I can't do both, you rogues? We'll see, we'll see. Wait till you're grandfathers yourselves."

"Then we'll say," said Jeff, "'I've often heard my grandfather tell stories which his grandfather's grandfather told him about Boston in 1630.'"

"Tut, tut, child. That's going too far back. I don't remember my grandfather's grandfather."

"And how would you like it," persisted Jeff, "if my little grandson should say to me, 'Well, grandfather, what was it that your grandfather told you at breakfast?' and I should have to say, 'My little grandson, my grandfather stopped telling me anything, because he wanted to eat his breakfast.' How little that would sound! As if one breakfast so far back could n't have waited!"

Grandfather Callender coughed a little, and looked at his daughter.

"Sally," said he, "get the boys off to school; it 's time they learned a little. Here, you young rascal of a Jeff, say this line after me before you go : —

    " 'Pater, avus, proavus, abavus, atavus, tritavus.'

Do you know what that means ? "

" *Pater* means father."

" And what does *avus* mean ? "

" Grandfather."

" Very good ; and *proavus ?* "

" I don't know, unless it 's great-grandfather."

" That 's right; you 're on the track ; now go ahead with the rest. *Abavus* comes next."

" *Abavus* means great-great-grandfather."

" Right, you 've got back to 1717, when your great-great-grandfather was born. *Atavus ?* "

" Great-great-great-grandfather."

" Right again. He was born in 1673. Now then for *tritavus.*"

" Great-great-great-great-grandfather," said Jeff, very deliberately.

" Well done, and so it is, for your *tritavus* was born in 1630. Now say the line again."

    " ' Pater, avus, proavus ' " —

" Well, go on. *Ab* " —

" ' — Abavus, atavus, tritavus.' "

" That's right.   Now, once more."

" ' Pater, avus, proavus, abavus, atavus, tritavus.' "

" Bravo, Jeff.   There are your ancestors all in a row, reaching from this breakfast room back to John Cotton's Boston.   Now say that line to yourself as you cross the Common on your way to school, and teach it to Benjy.   It will be worth all you will learn in school to-day.   And see if you can remember it till Saturday.   If you will, I'll pay you for it."

" What will you pay me, grandfather ? "

" Oh, you little bargainer.   You want to see if it will be worth while — do you?   I will tell you.   I have been thinking of it as we've been talking. Your school does n't keep Saturday afternoon.   Now if you and Benjy can each say that line to me without a false quantity Saturday, when you come back from school, I will take a walk with you in the afternoon, and show you a little of Boston."

" Why, grandfather," said Benjy, " we've always lived in Boston."

" You have, eh?   Ever since 1630?   But I have n't.   Then perhaps you'll show me.   I'd like to see the Boston that Winthrop lived in, and that Judge Sewall lived in, and Cotton Mather and Sam Adams and Ben Franklin."

" Oh, I know," said Jeff.   " You're going to show us some old houses, and tell us about Boston as it used to be — are n't you, grandpa ? "

"We'll see, we'll see. Can you walk as far as I can, d'ye think?

> " 'See saw, sacradown,
> Which is the way to Boston town?
> One foot up, the other foot down,
> And that is the way to Boston town.' "

Thereupon the old gentleman began to whistle and to walk hard round about the breakfast room, while his daughter laughed, and the boys clapped their hands.

"I'll remember the line, dear avus," said Jeff, "and I'll teach Benjy. Come, Benjy, we shall be late to school," and, snatching kisses and caps, away went the boys.

"Dear father, you will tire yourself with those boys," said his daughter, looking affectionately at him.

"Not a bit, Sally; and do you let me go my own way. I'll show them old Boston, my dear. Your boys must know the town. Latin's very well, and tops and skates, but the boy who lives in Boston and does n't know its history has never had a grandfather, you may be sure of that, or his grandfather was not worth anything. Why, if my old grandfather had n't — Bless that daughter of mine, if she has n't left the room! Never mind, she 's heard all my old stories, but the boys have n't, and they shall, aye, they shall hear them," and the old gentleman, who sometimes got excited, struck his hand down on the mahogany table.   A blue China plate was a little too near.

"I did n't mean to break that plate, Sally.   It was too near the edge of the table," and Grandfather Callender looked on meekly as his daughter, who had reëntered the room, picked up the broken bits.

CHAPTER II.

THE MAN BEFORE TRITAVUS.

THE Callenders always had an early dinner on the boys' account, and when Saturday came, and Grandfather Callender came into the dining-room, Jeff and Benjy were already in their seats.

"Get up, boys," said he; "you can't have your dinner till you've said your Latin line. Stand in a row," and they stood side by side in front of his chair.

"Say it together," and they said it in concert. Then he made them say it separately. He made them spell it forward and spell it backward.

"There!" he exclaimed. "You know that line now, you've got it by tongue. Let's see if you can get it by heart. We'll have our dinner now, and then we'll go out and invite the statue in Scollay Square to take a walk with us."

"I wish he would," said Jeff. "What a noise his bronze legs would make on the pavement. What is it, grandfather, that he holds, in his right hand? I suppose the book is his family Bible."

"It is the Charter of Massachusetts Bay Colony, with its great seal, Jeff. Winthrop and his friends" —

"Including Tritavus."

"Tritavus was born in 1630, the year Boston was founded. Winthrop was the man before Tritavus. I

did n't try to count your ancestors back of the first one born in old Boston, but his father came over in the ship with Winthrop."

"But what is the Charter, grandfather?" asked Benjy. "It looks like your college diploma rolled up."

"I will show it to you at the State House, some day. It was the parchment signed by King Charles I. of England giving certain people authority to set up a colony in Massachusetts Bay. Charles, who calls himself king of England,

Statue of Winthrop in Scollay Square.

land, Scotland, France, and Ireland, was held by English people to own a good part of North America.

He swept his hand up and down the country and said
' that belongs to me; ' and so whoever went from
England to settle on any of that land must first get
the king's consent. The Charter was his written
permission by which these people could plant a colony there, and choose managers of it, provided they
would remain good subjects of the king, not meddle
with any of the matters that belonged to him to
determine, and give a good account of themselves.
Those who had this permission of the king were
protected against any intruders, and as the king
was very powerful, it was very necessary to have his
Charter. Winthrop and his friends had spent a great
deal of money in getting ready for the settlement,
and they made sure that they would not be disturbed
in their plans, before they ventured. So when John
Winthrop is shown in the statue as stepping ashore,
with the Charter in his hand, it means that the men
who founded Boston held fast to their English ways
and English rights, and were not wild rovers who
wanted to get into the wilderness out of everybody's
way. The Charter meant a good, sound government
with the King of England behind it; and the Bible
in the other hand meant that Winthrop and his
friends intended to be governed by the law of God as
they read it there. They thought the king's Charter gave them land and an Englishman's home; but
they looked to the Bible to tell them how to live on
the land, and how to secure a place in the kingdom of

God, without which England or New England was no
better to them than the middle of Africa."

" Come, father," said the boys' mother, " you won't
eat your dinner if you keep talking."

"Keep preaching, you mean, Sally.   You think I
talk too much about these things, but I tell you they
are at the beginning of all honest history, and if I am
going to show this old town to the boys, I must " —

" Well, well, father, but please don't begin again.
The boys will be ready before you are."   There was
no delay on the old gentleman's part, for as soon as
dinner was over, and his key had fallen, they set out.
His key had fallen? Yes he always took a nap in his
chair after dinner, and when he composed himself for
sleep, held the door-key lightly between his thumb
and forefinger.   The moment he dropped asleep, his
muscles relaxed, the thumb and forefinger parted,
the key dropped upon a tile which he kept for the
purpose, and the sound waked him.   It was his alarm
clock set for the moment after he should fall asleep,
for he had a theory that all the refreshment of an
after-dinner nap lay in the single sensation of "losing
himself."   Sometimes his daughter, when she was
sure a little longer sleep would be good for him,
would softly push the tile a little to one side, and the
key falling on the Turkey rug would fail to wake
him.

To-day the boys sat in the window-seat until they
heard the key drop, when they jumped up, and their

grandfather with them, ready for their excursion. They went to Scollay Square to start, for there stood the bronze statue of Governor Winthrop, and if they could not take him with them, they could at least have a good look at him before they left him behind on his granite pedestal.

"He is looking in the general direction of his first house," said grandfather, "and we must see if we can find the remains of the first settlers. We'll start from Charlestown, where they started."

"Did people come to Boston by way of Charlestown?"

"How did they get to Charlestown without going through Boston?"

"That depends upon where they started from, Jeff. Winthrop and his companions came to Charlestown from Salem by land, and it would have been a very roundabout journey which took them through Boston."

"Then did n't they sail from England straight into Boston Harbor?"

"No. They sailed to Salem, where there was already a settlement formed by the same Massachusetts Company. At Salem they found Endicott and about two hundred others: a year before Thomas Graves, an engineer, had looked about for a place for a new town and had chosen Charlestown, and there about a hundred people were established. Winthrop did not think Salem a very pleasant place, so he and his

friends marched forward to Charlestown.   There was
one great house there at that time and a number of
wigwams; so Governor Winthrop and some of the
chief men were quartered in the Great House, and
the rest set up tents and booths and made log huts, I
suppose for temporary shelter."

The State House.

" Then, I suppose," said Benjy, " that they looked
across from Charlestown to Boston and liked the looks
of the place, and so went over."

" Something thus; but come, boys, we won't go
to Charlestown this afternoon; we'll go up to the
top of the State House, and get a bird's-eye view;

then perhaps you can see better how the place looked
when there were no houses on it." So they all turned
back from Bowdoin Square, which they had reached
while they had been talking, and climbed the hill to
the State House, and up the State House steps, through
the dome, and so to the cupola, at the top. They
chanced to be the only people there that day, and
though it was not perfectly clear they could see the
neighboring country fairly well.

"There," said grandfather, "if you look beyond
the wharves at the end of Charles River Bridge and
Warren Bridge you will see that the land rises toward Bunker's Hill. It was round the foot of that
hill that the first Charlestown was built, and only a
narrow strait separated Charlestown from this peninsula, and that strait of course was the Charles River.
But the distance was really greater than it is now.
Do you make out the gas-house over there?" and he
pointed toward Copp's Hill.

"Yes, sir."

"Well, now look over to where the Craigie Bridge
starts from on this side. Those two points were the
nearest to Charlestown, but between them was a great
bay or cove, which was partly water, partly marshy
land. It was shaped a little like a horseshoe, and
the head of the cove, which was called Mill Cove, was
about where Haymarket Square is now. An irregular
patch of solid ground, like a breakwater, stretched
across the broadest part of the cove, and afterward

people used it for a sort of stepping-stone to save them the necessity of going away round. They built a causeway over to this island from each point and so got across. But there was no causeway there then. What Winthrop saw, when he looked across Charles River from Charlestown, was a headland to the left, called Snow Hill, or Copp's Hill afterward; then a marshy cove, and to the right a series of bold hills shutting out his view of anything beyond. Our State House, where we are, stands on one of them, you know, but they have all been cut down and some of them altogether leveled. There were three hills in the centre grouped together, so much higher than the others that the people in Charlestown called the place Trimountain, a name which finally settled into our Tremont, and the Indians called it Shawmut."

"Were there Indians living here then?"

"No, not on this neck of land I believe. There was only one man living here at the time, and he was William Blackstone. Winthrop and his company expected to make Charlestown their home, but they only stayed there through the summer. They had a good deal of sickness, and at last the water seemed to be giving out in the springs. I don't know whether Winthrop had been across the river to explore the promontory, but one day Blackstone took a skiff and went over to Charlestown to see the governor and tell him that there were excellent springs in Shawmut, and to propose that all the people should

go there and settle. I should n't be at all surprised if
Winthrop went back with Blackstone and climbed
this very hill to see how the land lay. If he stood
here, he must have been almost as high as we are
now. He saw a lower hill farther down, occupied
now by Beacon and Mount Vernon streets, about
where Louisburg Square is, and on the western slope
was Blackstone's house. Near by was his spring, and
if Blackstone was with him he could have pointed
out three or four other springs, one where Pemberton
Square is now, and especially one at the head of
Spring Lane. When they were building the new
post-office they struck some running water which they
think comes from that spring, and they use it now
in the post-office. Then Winthrop saw how on the
other side of the peninsula was a great cove, with its
head at Dock Square, sweeping round to a good hill,
afterward known as Fort Hill, and he could look
across, as we are looking now, to the harbor, and then
by the narrow neck, which was scarcely wider than
Washington Street is now, that connected the peninsula with the main-land. This irregular piece of
ground, almost an island, covered with green grass
and a few trees, with springs on the hill-sides and
little brooks running down from them, with a broad
harbor in front and a high hill overlooking it, must
have seemed to him the very place for his settlement.
He saw Blackstone's house and orchard, and I think
he must have liked Blackstone himself who was a

3

quiet, bookish man, living alone by himself, as he had
lived for four or five years. And I think Blackstone
liked Winthrop, and was glad to have for a neighbor
this grave, wise man. Perhaps as he sat under his
trees, and looked across to Charlestown, he may have
seen them burying the poor people who died that
first summer. At any rate it was at his invitation
that Winthrop came over to Shawmut, and it was in
the early fall of 1630 that the people moved over."

"September 17," said Jeff, promptly.

"They must have gone over, some of them, at any
rate before that day, for it was on that day, the records tell us, that the General Court, which was sitting
in Charlestown, agreed to call Trimountain Boston."

"How many people moved over from Charlestown?" asked Benjy.

"I don't think it is possible to tell now, Benjy.
About a thousand came over with or directly after
Winthrop's coming, but of these a good many died,
and a good many stayed in Charlestown. I think
likely that the families moved over in parties before
winter, and that when Winthrop went it was pretty
well decided that Boston was to have the greater part
of the people."

"Did they all camp out on top of Beacon Hill?"
asked Jeff. "If I'd been here I'd have taken the
tip-top of the hill for my tent, and then when they
wanted the State House they'd have had to buy me
off."

" You would hardly have lasted as long as that, though you are a tough little fellow, Jeff, and besides I think you 'd have shown more good sense."

" Well, where did the man before tritavus build his hut ? "

" With the rest of the people, by what was afterward known as the Town Cove. You know I said there was a spring near the head of Spring Lane. That spring made the centre of the first settlement. People don't generally get on top of the highest hill when they settle in a new place ; they get under a hill for shelter if they can, but at any rate near good water for drinking, and if on the sea-coast near a harbor for their boats and fishing. Now that was just what Winthrop and his company did. There was the cove, ending on the right with a bluff hill, where they could plant a cannon ; behind them was a circle of hills, on which we are now ; and a good spring gave them the water they needed. So, you may think of the very oldest Boston as right down there **about the Old State House.** The houses were scattered along the shore of the cove. You know where Lewis Wharf is, though you can't pick it out very well from here. Well, if you follow from there along North Street up to the statue of Sam Adams, then turn down Dock Square, and keep to the right of Faneuil Hall, cross to State Street, keep along Kilby to Batterymarch, and then strike into Broad Street, and follow that to the foot of High Street,

you will just about follow the line of the old cove.
The Town Dock was where Faneuil Hall and Quincy
Market now stand. There, you can make out the
buildings from here, and only a few years ago you
could have seen Fort Hill near where you take the
boat to Hingham."

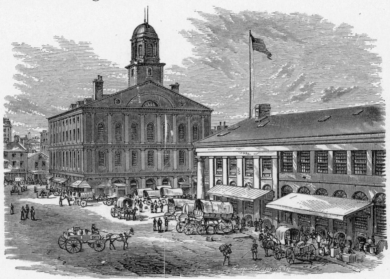

Faneuil Hall and Quincy Market.

" But they did n't stay always near the cove?"

" No, they followed the shore in each direction,
north and south, and spread over the peninsula. I
will tell you how you can remember the movement
of the town. Take the meeting-houses as they were
built, and they will show you the successive neigh-

borhoods. The First Church was built in 1632, —
a small thatched-roof, one-story building, which stood
on State Street, where
Brazer's Building now
stands. Eight years af-
terward it was replaced
by a larger building,
which stood where Joy's
Building, on Washing-
ton Street, now stands.
But come, boys, we

The First Church.

won't stay up here. We'll go down and see the
spot."

So down they climbed from the cupola of the
State House, and walked along the busy streets. It
was hard for the boys to imagine the Boston of 1630
as they walked down State Street and stood before
Brazer's Building and looked about them.

"Here stood the little church," said grandfather;
"and it was very near the houses of the first settlers,
you see; the water then came up nearly to this
point. Come a little farther down the street, and I
will show you how near." Then they walked as far
as Merchant's Row.

"What, only to here!" said Benjy.

"Yes, the first houses were about here. Here stood
Samuel Cole's tavern, the first built in Boston, about
half way, you see, between State Street and Faneuil
Hall. It was on the upper side of the street, looking

out on the water, and houses were about it. Now let us go to where the meeting-house stood when the people could afford to build a larger and better one." It was not a long walk to Joy's Building, and standing by it, they looked about to see what they could see.

"The old State House looks pretty old," said Benjy, with a critical air.

"Yes, but it takes the place of the first Town

The Old State House.

House, which was built there in 1658, a wooden building that stood on pillars; the market was held underneath. Now all this was the first great centre of the town. Here the people lived in houses with gardens about them and wharves by the water, and here opposite the Town House was the first shop, as below, a little way down, was the first tavern. We'll walk to the next centre of the town. As there came to be more inhabitants they could not all go to the same meeting-house, and in 1650 they built a second one." The walk to this took them through Dock Square again to North Street.

"Here stood, until twenty years ago," said grand-father, "an old building which every one was taken to see as the oldest house in town. I am not sure that it was the oldest even then, but it was so irregular and quaint that it had the name of the Old Cocked Hat. It had queer gables, ånd the upper story projected over the lower, and, although of wood, it was covered with a rough cast cement,

The Old Cocked Hat.

which was stuck full of old glass, coarse gravel, and odds and ends of things. We really see more of the old part of Boston when we get down here at the North End than anywhere else. North Street, on which we are walking, was in the time of your tritavus right along the shore of the cove. The street is occupied now by warehouses, but then wharves ran out from it, and it was occupied by houses and shops and ship-yards. Here we are at North Square, and this was the second great centre. Here stood the Second Church, which was built of wood, and known as the North Church. Some day we will explore other parts of the North End, but to-day we will make only one more visit on our way home, and that is to the Old South Church, which you know well enough. But why is it called Old South Church, Benjy?"

"I suppose because it is so old."

"And why is it called South, Jeff?"

"It is n't at the South End."

"But it used to be. If the First Church was near the head of State Street, it was in the centre of the town; the north was at the North End, and the south, at the head of Milk Street, was at the South End then. It was not called the Old South till the New South was built in 1715, at the foot of Summer Street. These three meeting-houses show the three centres of the town, at distances of twenty years. The First Church dates from 1630, the North from 1650, and the South, or third, from 1670, so you can have a pretty good idea of the general extent of Boston for the first half century. Essex and Boylston streets were about the southern limits. Tremont Street bounded it on the west, and most of the houses were at the North End and around the cove. There were no such streets as we now have. The people drove their cows to the Common, and up the sides of Beacon Hill ; they carried their grain to the mill at Copp's Hill, or at the foot of Summer Street, and the cart paths became by degrees the roads upon which houses were built. But here we are at the South Church. Close by it stood Governor Winthrop's house, which was taken down for firewood when the British occupied Boston at the beginning of the Revolution. Here the governor died, and when he died, twenty years after the settlement of the town, Boston was pretty well established. He was a great man. There were other notable people who came over with him, but he was the real leader of the town and colony ; and one reason why he was so good a governor of the colony was that he had learned to govern himself."

They had turned away from the church, and were soon crossing the Common, hurrying home for supper.

CHAPTER III.

THE HERMIT OF BOSTON.

THE next day was Sunday, and as they were walking home from church in the morning they came by Charles Street to the foot of Mount Vernon Street. Instead of turning up, grandfather kept on.

" Where are you going, grandfather ? " asked Jeffries.

" Come with me," he said, " a few steps; I want to show you something." So they all walked with him to Pinckney Street. " There ! " said he, " we are pretty near the water here, and at the foot of a tolerably steep hill. The town has not changed so much here as in some other places, but the hill has been cut away and used to fill up the low land on the river. Where we stand used to be rather a bold headland, which was called Blackstone's Point, for it was at the end of the farm of William Blackstone, who lived here four or five years before Winthrop came. The line of Charles Street was the boundary here of the Charles River. Just where his house was is not certain, but it was on this hill somewhere," — they were now climbing Pinckney Street, — " and most likely not far from his spring, which is thought to have been here at Louisburg Square. He came over probably about 1623, for after the Pilgrims went to Plymouth there was more than one attempt at settling on the shores of Massachusetts Bay before the great migration of Winthrop's company. Blackstone, however, was the only white man who lived on the peninsula of Boston, or Shawmut, as the Indians called it. He was a young man, only about twenty-eight years old when he came. He had been a student at Cambridge University in England; he was unmarried, and a shy man, fond of books, of which he brought a little library to this lonely place. Before Charlestown was settled he had only one or two white neighbors, — Thomas Walford, on the Mystic River, and Samuel Maverick, at Noddle's Island, which afterward became East Boston. I do not think he cared for neighbors, for it was not very long, only four or five years after Winthrop came, that he moved again, this time to a place in Rhode Island, near Lonsdale, where his grave is pointed out still. He named his place Study Hill, and occupied himself with his books and papers; but after his death these were all destroyed by the Indians, who burned his house during King Philip's war."

"Perhaps if they had been kept," said his daughter, "we should have known something more about him and about what he thought of Winthrop."

"No doubt, no doubt," said the old gentleman. "But he must have been on pretty good terms with

the people here, for he came back once in a while, —
it was only thirty-five miles away, — and he married
a Boston woman. He sold all his right to the land
here excepting six acres, and with the money bought
a stock of cows which he took to Study Hill."

" Let's go to Lonsdale some time," said Benjy,
" and dig about Study Hill. Perhaps old Mr. Blackstone buried his papers there, after all. Would n't
it be a famous thing to find them ! "

" We need n't go so far," said grandfather, poking
his key into the key-hole of the door, for they had
reached their own house. " I 've got them here."

" What ! "

" Yes, upstairs in my library. When I was a
youngster, though older than you boys, I used to imagine old Mr. Blackstone living at Lonsdale, among
his books and in his orchard, and wished I had his
papers. So, as the original ones were really burned
by the Indians, I made up a new set, — not as many
as he wrote, to be sure, — and I have a great mind
to read you a little from them. It won't be the real
thing, but we have to put up with a good deal of
make-believe nowadays. So this evening, after tea,
I will see what I can find among William Blackstone's
papers." .

It was as Grandfather Callender had said. He
had amused himself years before with keeping a
diary, imagining himself to be William Blackstone.
He had not looked at his papers for a long time, but

all this chat with the boys, and his walk yesterday, had brought the matter up freshly, and he went to his desk to find the diary. He found it, but found also with it, what he had forgotten, a little sketch which he had made of Blackstone's invitation to Winthrop to come over from Charlestown; and when he looked it over, he made up his mind that he would read that to the children instead of trying to entertain them with passages out of his imaginary diary. Especially he was willing to read it, because it would, perhaps, help the children to understand why Winthrop and his friends came across the Atlantic at all. So in the evening, after their early Sunday evening tea, when they had sung, " God bless our native land," grandfather put on his spectacles, sat erect in his leathern arm-chair before the fire, while the boys sat on stools with their heads in their mother's lap, and so read aloud his sketch of

WINTHROP'S VISIT TO BLACKSTONE.

It was a sultry day in August, 1630. The wind was blowing from the south, and whoever had work to do longed for some cool shade. A little line of huts and booths upon the north side of Charles River, under cover of the hill there, felt the full force of the hot sun and the warm breeze. There were sick men and women and children in the tents, who breathed with difficulty. They had few comforts or conveniences, and the water even which was brought to quench their thirst was warm and brackish. The figure of John Winthrop, a grave man, a little over forty years only in age, but looking old and care-worn already, was seen moving along the paths which led to the rude dwellings. He came finally to what was known as the Great House, where the principal men of the little colony lived until they should build houses for themselves and their families. He found his dear friend, Mr. Isaac Johnson, sitting in the doorway. He looked wearied and discouraged.

"You find me but a weight on our little plantation, I fear," he said, and rose as Mr. Winthrop came toward him.

"Nay, rest here, my good brother," said the governor, taking off his hat and brushing the hair back from his forehead. "We can ill afford to have you overcome with sickness; and this burning sun smites more fiercely than it was used to do in England."

"Truly; and I have been pondering the words, 'There shall be no sun there.' The Lady Arbella suffered much from this sultry heat."

"She has gone, indeed, to a better country. She plucked up her stakes to come into the wilderness; but it was only a brief passage through the desert to the Canaan that lies beyond."

"I have been looking at this narrow river," said Mr. Johnson, "and have half persuaded myself that it is a Jordan for our poor people of God, and that the promised land lies on the other side of it. Those high hills look as if they might give shelter from the sun and from the cold blasts which we must yet defend ourselves against. I fear much that I have grown restless since I parted with my dear wife."

" Have patience, good Mr. Johnson. I doubt not that the way will be made plain to us. I have myself looked across the river with some thought, and while you were absent in Salem, Mr. William Blackstone, who hath a dwelling there, came once to see me. He was a man of few words, but I gleaned from him that Mishawmut, as the Indians call Trimountain, was a fairer spot than this, and, moreover, that there was abundance of water there."

" I have a longing for a draught of pure water." At this moment, though they had heard no sound, they were aware of a silent, dusky figure standing before them. It was an Indian, who, when he had their attention, uttered no sound but handed to Mr. Winthrop a folded paper. The governor opened it and read it. His eye lighted, and he turned again to Mr. Johnson.

" It is from Mr. Blackstone. There is verily a strange Providence that while we were speaking of him this message should come."

" What saith he ? Read it ; the savage cannot understand."

" ' Worthy Mr. Winthrop. It grieves me to know that there hath been much sickness in your company, for so have I learned from good Mr. Fuller, and that more especially there is dearth of good water. It is not so here, but there are good springs and the country is pleasant to dwell in. If you will come hither with the Indian, I will show you the land. Your poor friend and servant, William Black-stone.'"

"It is friendly," said Mr. Johnson. "The hand of God is in it. I pray you go and spy out the land. Haply it may be a home for us."

The Indian had looked silently from one to the other, and with some awe at the bit of paper which he had brought. Now the governor turned to him, and motioned him to lead the way. The two passed down the path and entered the canoe which had been drawn up on the beach. The savage quickly paddled into the stream, and now taking advantage of the current, now bending his strength to resist it, made for the opposite shore. The governor felt the coolness of the breeze upon the water, but would fain have protected his head from the beating rays of the sun. They passed round a point, and, avoiding a marsh which edged the shore, brought up at the foot of a rough shoulder of a higher hill above them. There was a pebbly beach there, and a path climbed the acclivity. Up this went the Indian, followed by the governor. Arrived at the top, they were in a little upland valley, sheltered by a higher hill, and showing signs of cultivation. There was an orchard of young apple-trees, and a well worn path led to a spring a little further down. They were in sight, too, of a rude cottage of hewn wood, and, as they came to the door, the occupant rose, closed the book which he had been reading, and, placing it within, came out to receive his guest. The Indian turned away, and in a moment was invisible, having swift-ly descended the path by which he had just brought the white man.

Blackstone's House.

Mr. Blackstone was younger than the governor both in years and in countenance. He had a placid, thoughtful face, and he was dressed in a faded canon-ical suit, eked out by more incongruous dress. He stood thin and tall, and looked shyly aside as the governor stretched out his hand. He took it and led him to a rude bench in the shade of the house.

"You have a goodly garden here, Mr. Blackstone," said Winthrop. "It is a rest to my eyes to look upon it."

"It is my only companion save my books and my poor pen," said the recluse.

"It is a paradise indeed."

"Aye, and a paradise with apples in it," replied Blackstone, with a half smile. "I sometimes fear

4

there may be a temptation in this garden waiting
for me."

" There may even be temptation for one who lives
apart from his fellows," said the governor, gravely.

" True ; but I have escaped for the time at least
from what is trying England sorely now, the temptation of the lord bishops.   If I mistake not, your company has come hither for the same reason."

" We are not unmindful," said Winthrop, cau-
tiously, " of the advantage of being so far away from
the strife which is stirring in our poor church.   The
heathen are come into the inheritance of God, and
we sit by the waters of Babylon."

" Then you hope for a return to Jerusalem ? "

" It may not be in this generation," said the governor ; " and we know not but we are making a
place for the ark of the covenant to abide in."

" I am told that you have brought with you the
Charter of the king."

" We have brought it.   It was better so.   We
would be protected from our enemies, and they are
many."

" Mr. Winthrop," said the hermit, turning full upon
him, " I am a stranger to England now.   It is seven
years since I left her shores.   Tell me, what is to be
the end of these things ? "   The governor was silent
a moment.   Then he said : —

" Mr. Blackstone, it is not for me to foretell the
latter days.   We have, indeed, a goodly company of

us, separated ourselves from England, and have come into this wilderness. We could not see our children growing up under the anger of God. The king has evil counselors. The church is dragged away from the God of Israel by the carnally-minded bishops. It was time to come out from the ceiled houses and dwell in tents. Here we have made a covenant with our God, and we trust here to keep the unity of the spirit in the bond of peace. We are brethren knit together in one communion, and if we live and occupy this land, I trust it may yet be said of succeeding plantations, ' The Lord make it like that of New England.' "

" Then it is a new England that you would make here ? "

" Yes, it is a new England."

" And will the king suffer you to live in peace ? "

" We have the King of kings on our side, and we have his majesty's Charter." Blackstone half concealed a smile.

" It is well to have safeguards. Does the Charter define your government ? If you come hither to live on my land, know that I occupy under Sir Ferdinando Gorges' patent ; and, I crave your pardon, but what manner of laws have you made for your government ? "

" We have a covenant, and we are governed by the laws of England and by the Word of God."

" And you will leave me in peace here in my orchard ? "

"We can have no quarrel with you, good Mr. Blackstone. We will buy your title to so much land as you will part with, if it seem wise and well to bring the company hither."

"I doubt it not," said the hermit, rising. "If it please you, and you are rested, come with me and I will show you the land." The two climbed the high hill back of the house, and from its summit looked off upon the sparkling water of the bay, and down upon the other side upon the poor little settlement at Charlestown. They walked down the slope, and, avoiding the marshy places, came to the cove which received the waters of the bay upon the eastern shore of the peninsula. Winthrop's eye followed the shore from there.

"That might be a well fortified place," he said presently, pointing to the rough hill which afterward became Fort Hill.

"Then you fear enemies?" said Blackstone, slyly; "enemies that come by water?"

"We are encompassed about by foes," said the governor. "We expect no peaceful, continuous possession here." Blackstone led him to the bubbling spring, near which Winthrop afterward placed his house, and as they turned away they went toward the high hill again. They stopped a moment at its foot and looked about them. They were in one of the greenest, pleasantest spots they had seen, and Winthrop, taking a broken stick which lay near, thrust it into the ground where they stood.

"This shall be our most worthy Mr. Johnson's lot," said he, pleasantly. "He is the first settler here after you, Mr. Blackstone." The hermit did not reply. In truth, when Mr. Winthrop drove the stake into the ground he felt a sharp pain in his mind, as if his quiet life was now rudely broken in upon. He had felt a pity for the unfortunate company, and in his compassion had suddenly offered to give up his tranquil home, but now that he was taken at his word he as suddenly repented. He was silent for the rest of the walk and a moodiness came over him.

"You will find us peaceful neighbors," said the governor as he finally left him on the shore, where the Indian was in waiting with his boat.

"It may be," said the hermit to himself as he turned away, "but I fear much that I have escaped the tyranny of the lord bishops to fall into that of the lord brethren, and that I shall like these latter no better than the others. But I like this Mr. Winthrop. He is a just man and fears God, and indeed if the worst comes I can move myself farther away. The wilderness has many solitary places."

The governor after he had once seen the peninsula had no longer any doubt that it was wise to move the company thither. They were not all prepared to go, and some who had already staked out their farms in Charlestown resolved to remain there, but the more part gladly made ready to sit down, as they termed it, across the river. Of these Mr. Isaac Johnson was one. He had a great longing to get there, and spoke often to Mr. Winthrop while the preparations were going on.

"I could almost believe," he said one day, "that there I should be nearer to my dear wife."

"It is not far hence to where the Lady Arbella is," said Winthrop, "and I would that we might make the place a memorial to her. It was in Boston that she lived, as did many of our company. There, too, is our beloved Mr. Cotton; and since the larger part of us are from Lincolnshire, it is right fitting that we should give the new plantation that name." And so it was determined, and the record was made on the 17th of September, "that Trimontaine shall be called Boston," and so this day of the month is the baptismal day of the old town. Mr. Isaac Johnson, as the days went by, drooped and could not be removed. He died while the rest were one by one passing across to the new settlement, and thither his body was borne and buried where he would have lived. He was the first to be laid away there, and the ground was hallowed by his sepulture. So one after another desired to be laid beside him, and the old burying-ground about King's Chapel became the first resting place on the peninsula.

"And was Mr. Blackstone buried there?" asked Benjy

" No, he was buried, as I said, at his new home in Rhode Island.   He grew uneasy as the peninsula became a busy thrifty settlement.   It was no longer the place for a hermit.   It had become the chief town of the New England which Winthrop and his fellows desired to see."

CHAPTER IV.

A DAY WITH JOHN WINTHROP.

THAT evening, after tea, as the boys and their mother and grandfather sat before the fire in the library, the talk fell upon the old Boston which they had walked about in the afternoon.

"Would n't John Winthrop be surprised," said Benjy, "if he really could step down and walk along Court Street!"

"I think the people standing there would be the most astonished," said Jeff.

"Oh you know what I mean. Of course if he could step down, no one would be surprised at that, but how odd Boston would look to him. He would think himself back in London, would n't he, grandpa?"

"I think he would be puzzled to see the likeness to the London which he left in 1630, for the Boston of to-day is very different from the London of two hundred and fifty years ago. The people, for instance, on Court Street to day are dressed quite the same as those on the Strand, but you noticed how differently Winthrop appeared."

" But does n't the sculptor dress him in robes which look better than the common dress ? " asked the boys' mother.

" Sculptors are apt to take what advantage they can of a possible graceful dress, in place of an ugly familiar one, but I don't think there is much difference in this case. That stiff ruff was worn about the neck, as you see it in the statue ; the shoes were low and peaked, and large knots or rosettes were worn at the instep. In place of the coat, waistcoat, and trousers, there was a doublet, not unlike a loose frock, gathered about the waist with a belt, and under that a waistcoat, to which was fastened what was known as trunk-hose coming to the knees, and then long stockings reached up to meet the trunk-hose. The sleeves of the doublet were often slashed, that is cut with open bands, to show the linen beneath, and a cloak or mandilion was worn over all. Winthrop was probably moderate in his dress, for he set an example to others in his way of living, but some of the richer colonists used to wear gold and silver lace. I wonder that the sculptor has made Winthrop wear low shoes instead of great boots which were worn then by gentlemen, and would seem to have been more appropriate to one landing from a ship."

" I think the ruff was ugly," said Jeff, " and I think it must have been worse than a stand-up collar. I have seen old gentlemen wearing collars which looked as if they might saw off their ears."

"Don't make fun of your old grandfather, you rogue! But the collars which we wear now are the old ruff which has grown smaller and smaller. Besides, the ruff was worn by gentlemen, by those who were of better birth and who did not work with their hands, or if they worked dressed themselves very differently for the time they did work. The common colonist's dress was different from the gentleman's. In place of a ruff he wore bands, or a kind of broad flat collar with cord and tassel; then his clothes were of much coarser material; his breeches were made of leather, he had a leathern girdle, his clothes were fastened together with hooks and eyes, and his coarse shoes had wooden heels. His hat was lined with leather, and his dress generally was to stand hard usage. At that time there was a much sharper distinction between different classes, and people were addressed according to their rank in life. There was only now and then a lord or baronet in Boston; the highest title was Mr. or Mrs., and that title was given only to certain people. The governor and the higher magistrates and ministers were addressed as Mr. and their wives as Mrs., but the great body of people were called Goodman or Goodwife, and servants had no title at all. When a man who was called Mr. had disgraced himself, he lost the title of Mr. and became Goodman; and if a Goodman fell away, I think he lost that title."

"Father," said his daughter, "I wish you would

give us an idea of how a person lived in Boston in the early days of the colony. Take a Mr. and a Goodman and a servant."

"And a boy," added Jeff.

"One would think they were all males in Boston," said grandfather.

"Oh, you could n't tell about the men and boys without saying something about the women and girls."

"Well," said the old gentleman, after reflecting a moment, "I should like to do it, but you must give me a little time to think it over, for it is not altogether easy to tell. You see the people of that time in Boston, although they kept records and diaries, did not at first tell very much about the little things which now interest us ; they had a great deal more to say about their discussions in church, and you would not care so much about that, but I will see what I can do."

It was two or three evenings after this that Grandfather Callender said he was ready to tell them what he knew of the way people lived in Boston in 1649.

"That was nearly twenty years after the town was settled, you know," he said ; "and I have taken that time because in twenty years things had become pretty well established, and there were boys and girls growing up who had never seen England, yes, and children born whose mothers and fathers had no recollection of England, but only knew Boston and Boston life. Besides it was the year when Governor John Winthrop died, and I never think of Boston in those earliest days without thinking of that man who was the best example of the founders of our old town. As long as he lived he was the chief man, and his word and life had a great deal to do in giving character to the town. Let me try to picture what one of John Winthrop's days may have been during the last year of his life.

" He lived, as you remember I told you, where the Old South Church now stands, in a two-story wooden house. A garden was about it, and from the windows he could look out upon the harbor and the islands with their farms, which were dotted about. His children were grown and no longer lived with him; his son John was Governor of Connecticut; in his loneliness he had married again, and he and his wife lived alone in the house. He had some land, but the greater part of his property was gone. He was Governor of Massachusetts, and so the chief magistrate of the colony, and his time was divided between his private and his public affairs. We will suppose it to be a Thursday : the morning bell had rung at half after four, when, I have little doubt, the governor and his household rose ; after breakfast the governor walked along the road from his house to the market-place, where now stands the old State House. Here the farmers from the neighboring country had brought

in their vegetables and fruit, although the gardens
and orchards in town furnished most that the gentlemen needed for their tables; here, too, were the meat
and the game which the Indians and farmers' sons had
shot and trapped. The meal which the governor's
wife used was from grain grown, I suppose, on their
out of town farm at Ten Hills, on the Mystic, and
brought to the windmill on Copp's Hill, or to that
which stood where the West Church on Cambridge
Street now stands, or perhaps to that near the foot of
Summer Street. A green lane led from it by the
water-side, and up what is now Milk Street, to the
governor's garden, and if he were walking he may
have come upon his wife, pail in hand, going to the
spring near by for water. Perhaps, when he had
been through the market, he went down the road that
led to the water, and coming near the site of the first
meeting-house, stopped to speak with William Davis,
at his apothecary shop, about the pump which Mr.
Venner and some neighbors wanted to place near by;
it would need to be talked over in General Court. He
may have gone a little farther to the inn of the Three
Mariners to see the innkeeper, and be sure that there
had been no disorder about the house; to say a word
to some idler sunning himself on the wharf: he had
himself in his own house long set the example of
sobriety by declining to have healths drunk at the
table, and lately a law had been passed making it a
penal offence. If he continued his walk to the Town

Dock he would inquire what news had been heard of the fishing vessels, or of those which traded to the West Indies: he had for his part a little venture in the Blessing of the Bay, which he had built, the year after the settlement, near his farm on the Mystic: they might be looking for a ship from London with news from home. If the ship came in the master would carry Mr. Winthrop's letters to him, and bring him news of the war in England, for this was when King Charles I. was fighting the Parliament, and there were anxious men among his subjects in Boston. His walk would take him along the shore to Captain Nehemiah Bourne's ship-yard, near where Union Wharf is now; he had been one of three men appointed to look the ground over near Captain Bourne's house, to determine on a proper place for building a ship, and the business was growing and prospering.

"Very likely he was to attend a meeting of the Great and General Court, and would go in the middle of the morning to the meeting-house to meet there the other magistrates and the ministers. Possibly as he went in he passed by the stocks and saw a poor drunken wretch sitting behind it with his feet and hands thrust through the holes, and his head hanging down for shame. In those days men who offended against the laws were punished in their persons more than they are now; they were whipped at the whipping-post, made to stand on the pillory, or sit in the stocks, or have their feet chained in the bilboes. They were held to have done that for which they should be ashamed, and so they were punished in a way to bring them to shame, for every one that went along the road could see them in this sorry plight. The poor Indian was very often in the stocks, for many of the laws were not very intelligible to him.

"It was in the meeting-house, I think, that the General Court was held, and all sorts of questions would come up before it, — questions which are not now discussed in our legislature, but which did not seem out of place in a meeting-house. The magistrates and the people for whom they were making laws were as much members of churches as they were towns-people, and they settled religious affairs in the General Court. There were, to be sure, a good many in the earliest days who were not church members, and these had nothing to say about the government. Only those who were members of churches had a right to vote, for Winthrop and his friends were trying very hard to have a state which should be governed exactly according to the will of God, and they thought that only those who were bound together in their churches were able to know just what that will was. They made mistakes, but they were not the mistakes of men who were selfish or seeking to get some advantage over others.

"It may be that on his way home to dinner Gov-

ernor Winthrop stopped to see Mr. Woodbridge, at
the school-house in School Street, where King's Chapel
stands.   The street was hardly more than a lane
leading up to Centry Hill, but the little school-house
stood on it, and so it got its name.   The school-master
had fifty pounds a year and a house to live in; he
had one usher, too, to help him.   The school was for
boys, and they were taught Latin, for in a state which
guarded its church so jealously, great care was taken
that the race of learned men should never die out.
The boys, no doubt, had to study hard, but they had
plenty of fun I am sure after school was out.   Think
of trapping rabbits and hunting foxes at the back of
Beacon Hill, and what famous slopes there were for
coasting down in those days, straight away with no
houses about.   They had work enough, too, — work
in the fields and on the wharves, for the town looked
out that there should be no idlers.   If fathers and
mothers did not set them to work, the magistrates did.

" When Mr. Winthrop went home to dinner it is
very likely that his wife had a story to tell him of
some family in need.   He looked after his poorer
neighbors as other of the chief men did.   He thought
it a sin to let his neighbor suffer.   There is a pretty
story told of him shortly after they had moved over
to Boston from Charlestown.   No ship had come in
for a long time, and they had passed a severe winter,
the people being so poor that they were forced to
live on clams and mussels, acorns and ground-nuts.

You see they had not yet been able to plant the ground and reap a harvest, and their provisions had given out. The governor had his last batch of bread in the oven, and was at his door-way giving the last handful of meal in his barrel to a poor man who had none, when suddenly off in the harbor appeared the long-looked for ship ; and so on that twenty-second of February they had a Day of Thanksgiving, for their Thanksgiving and Fast Days were not on certain regular days, but were appointed from time to time whenever the people had anything notable to give thanks for, or to be sorry for. There is another story told by Cotton Mather, which I will read to you," and grandfather took down Mather's Magnalia from the shelf.

" ' There was one passage of his charity that was perhaps a little unusual : in an hard and long winter, when wood was very scarce at Boston, a man gave him private information that a needy person in the neighborhood stole wood sometimes from his pile ; whereupon the governor, in a seeming anger, did reply, " Does he so ? I 'll take a course with him ; go, call that man to me. I 'll warrant you I 'll cure him of stealing." When the man came, the governor considering that if he had stolen it was more out of necessity than disposition, said unto him : . " Friend, it is a severe winter, and I doubt you are but meanly provided for wood ; wherefore I would have you supply yourself at my wood-pile till this cold season

5

be over." And he then merrily asked his friends,
whether he had not effectually cured this man of
stealing his wood ?'

" He was very ready indeed to provide for the
needy, and grew poor by reason of giving so freely
from his own store. In after days the town built a
granary where Park Street Church now stands, and
the name remains with the burying-ground next to
it. There grain was stored, and the poor could buy
at a price very near cost.

" We have been playing that it was Thursday.
Thursday was market-day, and it was also Lecture-
day. One of the ministers gave a lecture in the
meeting-house, and when you think that the people
were set on having a perfect church and a perfect
state you will understand that they were ready to
give their time when not at work to hearing their
ministers and pondering knotty questions. Nothing
seemed to them of so much importance as ordering
their lives according to the law of God, and they
wanted something that should tell them just what
that law was. They thought the Bible the most important book possible for this, and as they believed
themselves to be chosen by God to be brought into
this wilderness, so they read especially that part of
the Bible which told of the children of Israel and
their difficulties, and tried to make the rules which
were given to the Jews fit their case. Those rules
were based on great and lasting laws, so that the

Puritans in Boston, while often wrong in seeking to apply Jewish rules to New England men and women, never got very far away from wholesome truths, and they believed with all their hearts that everybody in Boston should be upright and fear God, that the children should be obedient, and that whoever did wrong should be punished; and they wanted every-one to think just as they did. They were downright English people, — stubborn, and unable to see how anybody could differ from them and be right.

"Now, the day over, we can imagine Mr. Winthrop at home writing a letter to his son John, the Governor of Connecticut. Upon the wall hangs the portrait of him, said to be by the famous painter Van Dyck, and now in the Senate Chamber at the State House. His books, forty or fifty in all, are in a chest or on some shelves. At his death they were given to Harvard College, but were all burned in 1764, in the fire which destroyed the old Library; we have a list of them, and can see that his reading was chiefly in the old Latin classics, or in Latin or English commentaries on the Bible. If it was winter there was a fire on the hearth, for stoves had not yet come in, and candles burned on the table. He had received letters from his son by an Indian messenger. There was no regular postal system, and people depended on chance travelers or on such messengers as might be sent on purpose. It was a common thing to employ Indians, who were hardy and fleet, on such errands. This Indian may have been bidden wait for the return letters, and the governor writing to his son would tell him the latest news he had received from England, — news which to-day the plainest person could read in his morning newspaper, but which then came laboriously by ship only to the chief men ; and Mr. Winthrop would repeat what he had heard to his son, not as a bit of gossip, but because it might make a world of difference to them and their colonies whether Cromwell or Charles were victorious. 'The news out of England,' he writes at one time ' is very sad ; all the counties are for the king save Yorkshire ;' and then, 'Our news is sad at home also : God hath visited our family and taken from us your good sister Adam ;' that is, Adam Winthrop's wife ; and so he would go on to give news of the family and a little account of business. But his letters were chiefly of public affairs, for when he came to America and engaged in the new colony it was not so much to mend his own fortunes, which would have fared better in England, but because he would help forward a settlement where God's people could live honest lives.

" While the governor was writing, the Indian messenger was maybe hobnobbing with the governor's servant, who was an Indian. The Indians were sometimes taken as servants and trained, but the colonists had hard times with these wild men. The governor and others like him were quite as anxious to teach them religion as to get proper service out of

them, but the people were in constant fear in the
early days of the colony lest the Indians should prove
treacherous, and they made stringent laws, by which
it was necessary to get permission of the Court to
keep an Indian, and
fire-arms and even
sticks were forbid-
den them.

Statue of Winthrop at Mount Auburn.

"At length the
nine o'clock bell
rang, as it has con-
tinued to ring al-
most to this day, and
covering up the fire
with the ashes, and
having his evening
devotions, the gov-
ernor's day was
ended."

It was pretty plain
that the children's
day was ended too.
Benjy was fast asleep,
and though Jeff was
sitting bolt upright, his eyes had a fixed look which
showed that he was trying hard to keep awake but
could fall asleep in an instant.

"Wake up, Benjy!" cried his grandfather. "My
sermon is ended. Go to bed, boys; I can't expect

youngsters to care as much for these things as I do, but it won't do you any harm to hear a little of them; and for my part I'm glad that when I lay my old bones away in Mount Auburn, Governor Winthrop will be sitting up all night for me in the chapel, with his hands clasped on his knee."

"Making a sound like money jingling," said his daughter.

"O Sally, Sally! That's just what I have thought, but I never said it."

CHAPTER V.

THE RED INDIAN AND THE PALE FACE.

IT happened about this time that there were public meetings held in Boston in behalf of the Ponca Indians, and the newspapers had much to say about their wrongs. The children came home one day in some excitement, for they had met Miss Bright Eyes on their way home from school.

"We knew it was she," said Jeff eagerly, "for Jack Eliot, who was with us, heard her speak the other evening, and he took off his hat to her."

"Yes," said Benjy, "and she bowed and smiled back at him and at us."

"Now that was curious," said grandfather. "I wonder if she knew his name."

"Whose? Jack's?"

"Yes."

"I don't believe she did. He's one of the big boys, but he does n't know many of the fellows. He used to live in Roxbury."

"Of course he did," said grandfather greatly amused. "Tritavus met him there, and Atavus might have seen him an old man, when Atavus was a school-boy like you, Jeffries."

" Oh, you are talking of one of Jack's ancestors I suppose."

" I don't know if he can trace his family back to John Eliot, the Apostle to the Indians ; but if he can he ought to be proud."

" I 've heard of him," said Benjy. " He made a Bible for the Indians."

" Yes, and so rare are the copies now that when one is sold, it brings more than a thousand dollars."

" I should n't think there would be any Indians rich enough to pay that," said Benjy. " The only ones I ever saw at Bangor could never have bought it."

" And the man who does buy the Indian Bible cannot read it," said grandfather. " He only buys it as a curiosity."

" What little trace the Indians have left of themselves about here," said the boys' mother.

" Very little indeed. The name Shawmut is almost the only sign of them in Boston."

" There 's India Wharf," said Benjy.

" Hoh ! " said Jeff.

" Benjy is not so far out of the way, Jeff. You know the Indians here got the name because the first voyagers thought they had found India when they found America."

" Then there is Indian corn."

" Yes, and Indian file. When you boys walk in Indian file, you are using a name that came from the way our ancestors said Indians went through the woods, where they had to ' go one abreast ' as an old writer says."

" But, grandfather, were there never any Indians in Boston ? "

" None were living here when Winthrop came, or Blackstone before him, so far as we know, but for all that the town bought its land of the Indians."

" I thought Blackstone sold it to the town."

" So he did, but long afterward it turned out that when Winthrop came to Boston Chickataubut, who was the most prominent Indian in the neighborhood, made a deed to the English of all the land on the peninsula. It was half a century from the settlement of Boston that anything was said about it, and it was a good many years after that before the deed was recorded. I suppose Winthrop wanted to secure as good a title as possible. They had the Charter, and Blackstone's deed and Chickataubut's, and besides they had possession of the land, and that was, perhaps, the strongest claim of all."

" But were n't there Indians about Boston ? "

" Oh yes ; no one could travel to Plymouth, or any of the neighboring settlements, without meeting them. They hunted and sold their game to the whites ; they were their messengers, as I told you the other day ; they sometimes were servants, and they liked, some of them, to stroll about the town, and, I am sorry to say, they caught the vices of the town very readily. Do you remember Samuel Cole's tavern that I told you about ? "

" It was on Merchant's Row."

" Yes, and there in 1636 the governor entertained Miantonomah, an Indian sachem, who visited Boston. Nowadays, you know, when a distinguished person comes to town as a guest of the city, he is provided with rooms at the Brunswick, or Parker House, or some other hotel, and a dinner given him. It's the same thing. It was just the same in 1631, when Governor Winthrop entertained Chickataubut at his own house. I suppose he would like to have sent him to an inn, but there was none then, so he had him at his table, and gave him cheese and pease when he went away. Chickataubut gave him a hogshead of Indian corn, and Winthrop sent him to the tailor's and gave him a full suit of clothes. I don't believe an Englishman like Winthrop relished such close quarters with a wild Indian, but the town was weak, and they must needs keep on good terms with their neighbors. Besides, the best of the whites really did want to treat them as their neighbors, to do as they would be done by; and in their laws they tried to be perfectly just between a white man and an Indian."

" But they got into fights," interrupted Jeff.

" Yes, they got into fights, and there was more than one reason. No doubt the chief reason was, that the white man showed that he was pushing his settlements this way and that, and the Indian began to be alarmed lest he should be crowded out. Then the white man's laws were very stringent; they were hard for the whites, but they bore harder upon the Indian, because he was not used to laws at all, and could not understand why the white people should insist upon a great many things that meant nothing to the red man. And then the white men did not understand the red men any better than the red understood the whites. At that time people were much more afraid of what they could not see than of what they could ; it is always so, but it was much commoner then than now to believe in all manner of evil spirits. You study in your mythology of the crowds of spirits which the Greeks and Romans imagined to be living in woods and rivers and seas, and on hills and mountains. Well, the English had a mythology which was not quite so clear and well understood ; and when they saw the dark woods about them, and these dusky Indians coming and going, they were ready to believe that the Indians were not more than half men and women ; so they thought often that they were doing right in getting rid of them."

"Boston never was attacked by Indians — was it, grandfather ?"

"No. It could not have been easy for the most hostile Indians to get at the town. It was protected by water on all sides, and only the narrow neck connected it with the main-land. There they had a guard, and very soon after the settlement they built a barricade, and had a gate which was shut in the evening, after which no persons could come in. Then they forbade Indians carrying fire-arms, or even sticks, within the town.   No, Boston was safe enough ; but it was more than once called upon to send men to the Indian wars.   The solitary farm houses near Boston had stockades about them, and the villages were

A Stockade.

guarded.   I think the nearest that the Indians ever came to Boston in their marauding was when they attacked and burned Medfield.   In the war which was known as King Philip's War, in 1675, it is said that eight hundred and fifty men marched from Boston as part of the little army which defeated Philip."

"It must have been like some of our frontier life now," said the boys' mother.

"Very much like it in some things, and in this among others, that while there was all this enmity between the white man and the red man, there were some white missionaries who were trying their best to bring the Indian out of his savage state, and the Indians whom they had Christianized became the white man's best friends in the terrible fighting which followed, whether in King Philip's War or among the Sioux."

"John Eliot was the best known of the missionaries — was he not, father?"

"Yes.   John Eliot here, and Thomas Mayhew in Martha's Vineyard.   John Eliot was almost a Bostonian. He was a minister in Roxbury, and lies buried there, but his fame is for his devotion to the Indians. He tells us how he went with three others to Newton to hold a meeting with the Indians, and tried to 'screw, by a variety of means, something or other of God into them.' He studied their language patiently, and preached to them, and translated the Bible into their tongue ; but I really think that he taught them more about God by his own unceasing kindness toward them than he ever did by his sermons. There is no argument so powerful as a man, and Eliot gave himself for the Indian. When the war came it was found that the praying Indians, as his converts were called, clung to the whites, and separated themselves from their wild fellows.

" After Eliot began, there was a continuous effort to make Christians of the Indians, and the people who had the work in charge thought there was no surer way than to teach them out of the same books which they used for their own children. So the psalm books and catechisms and sermons which held what the Boston people thought to be the only true way of religion were translated into Indian and given to the red men. They built a college for them at Cambridge, so you see they were very much in earnest. It seems to us that they went to work without understanding the poor red men, and that they began at the wrong end with their teaching ; but they knew no other way, and I think it helps us to understand the men who laid the foundations of Boston, when we see how doggedly the best of them set to work with the Indians to make them into Puritans. It shows how entirely convinced they were that their way was the only true way."

"Talk a little Indian, grandfather," said Benjy.

"That's more than I can do," said he, "but I will read you one word," and he put on his spectacles, took down a book, and read slowly and with great emphasis, —

"'Nuk-kit-te-a-mon-te-a-nit-te-a-on-ga-nun-no-nash.'

There, what does that mean, Benjy?"

"I should think, from the way you read it, it meant, 'Your money or your life.'"

"Some kind of a vegetable," suggested Jeff.

"It means 'our mercies.'"

"Well, I think it is one of Nuk and so forth that we don't have to learn that word, and decline it at the Latin School. Why, it's almost as long as the new building."

J. C. CONANT BOSTON.

LATIN AND ENGLISH HIGH SCHOOLS.

CHAPTER VI.

THE LITTLE REVOLUTION.

ONE day about Thanksgiving time the children came home from Roxbury, where they had been with Jack Eliot, and they had much to tell of what they had seen, — more especially of the old Parting Stone in Eliot Square, a large stone which bears upon its face the words, " The Parting Stone, 1744, P. Dudley," and stands at the meeting of two ways which were the old roads to Dedham and to Cambridge.

"There used to be several mile-stones in Roxbury," said grandfather, " and some are yet standing, which were planted by Paul Dudley. He was a son of Joseph Dudley, a man bitterly hated in his time by many, yet who, from the time he was twenty-five till nearly seventy years old, was in some office or held some important trust. It was in his time that the Revolution occurred."

" Why, I don't understand that, grandfather," said Jeff. " It says 1744 on the Parting Stone, and the stone was set up by Joseph Dudley's son. How could Joseph Dudley have been living in 1776 ?"

" Oh, we have n't got as far as the American Revolution, Jeff. It is the Boston Revolution that I mean. Did you ever hear of that?"

" No, sir."

" Then I will tell you about it. You know the statue of Winthrop shows him with the Charter in his hand, and I have told you how much value the people set on the Charter. It was the king's warrant for them to carry on the government and hold the land, and as long as they held this parchment they thought themselves able in Boston to elect their governor and other officers, and to manage things as they wished. They did not want to be governed by England, at such a distance, and they did not want men sent over to govern them who might not care for the things they cared for, and would very likely interfere with their churches and their ways. They had now for fifty years been governing themselves under the Charter. The Charter was a convenient paper. It was not very explicit, and the people used it in such a way that it should give them the largest possible liberty. All the while they called themselves loyal servants of the King of England, and they helped him in his wars with the French, and sent timber for his ships, and made him presents, and did all they could to keep on good terms with him, so that they might be left to themselves. It was King Charles the First who was on the throne of England when Winthrop came over; but while Boston was growing, changes were taking place at home.

Charles was beheaded, and the Parliament had the power, with Oliver Cromwell at the head. Cromwell was Protector, and the New England men were his friends, though they were careful not to become too entangled in English affairs. But Boston men had had a good deal to do with bringing forward the Commonwealth in England; the success of the experiment over here had made Englishmen who were of their way of thinking more sanguine that England, too, could do without a king, and have a church without bishops; and when Charles II. came to the throne, his advisers, who did not like Puritans and Puritan ideas, began to urge the king to make himself more felt in America. 'See that Boston,' they said; 'it is growing rich and independent. They make their own laws there, and coin money, and keep an army, and they will not let Church of England men have any rights. They are getting too independent, and you might as well have no authority at all there as to have the name only and not the real thing. They pretend that the Charter gives them all their power. Then call back the Charter. It never was intended to give away a great and rich country.' So the king began to be persuaded, and sent over to Boston for the Charter. This was just what the people did not wish to give up, so they made excuses, all the while protesting their loyalty to the king, sending him presents, and trying by all means to evade his demand. It took a long while for letters and persons to cross the Atlantic. There was plenty to occupy the king, and he was finding it necessary to keep a strong army in England. He could not go to war with his own colony, which was constantly saying that the king was their great and glorious master. He went to law with them, and demanded the Charter through the courts ; but year after year the magistrates in Massachusetts succeeded in keeping the Charter without refusing the king's order point blank. It became harder and harder, however, and there were partisans of the king in Boston who were making trouble between him and New England. Probably some busy merchants, too, thought it was making much ado about nothing, and that if they were to give up the Charter they would still go on as they always had ; that even if the king sent over governors, these could do no harm, and perhaps trade would be even better.

" At length it became necessary to send over two men to London as commissioners to look after the interests of Massachusetts. One of these was Joseph Dudley, who had held high office, and was thought to be an able and honest man. These commissioners, however, could not prevent the king and his advisers from having their way ; and at length, without getting the actual Charter back into his hands, the king's court declared that it was no longer in operation, that the colonies of New England were thenceforth to look directly to the king and the laws of England, and were to be governed as a piece of property belonging to the crown. The man who came back with this news, and brought a commission from the king, was Joseph Dudley, who had made friends in England, and had been appointed President of New England until a royal governor should be sent. The next year the governor came, — Sir Edmund Andros, — and the colonies of New England became the Province of New England.

"It was not merely a change of names. The General Court, which had been elected by the people of the towns, ceased to exist when the Charter was taken away and Dudley was made President. The whole authority was now centred in the king, and was delegated by him to the governor, who had a council appointed by the king to help him. The king's name was felt everywhere ; courts were held, taxes laid, laws passed, all in the name of the king ; and, what alarmed the people still more, the governor gave out that the titles to the land which the people held were good for nothing unless freshly granted by the king. It looked as if all the work which had been done for sixty years was to be swept away.

"For a time everything seemed to be going on as Andros wished. The people murmured, and some, who objected, were thrown into prison ; but, on the whole, Boston appeared to submit to its loss of liberty. No one seemed to know just what to do, or how to take this new order of things. They saw the Church

of England set up.   Very few of the people then
living in Boston had ever seen the Church of England, and there was a great deal of curiosity about
it, for they knew that it was because Winthrop and
their fathers thought this church in error, and growing worse, that they had come over and settled Boston.   Then, besides being curious, they hated it, for
they heard their ministers speak of it as something to
be detested."

"Was King's Chapel built then, father?"

"Not at first, for the Church of England men used
the Town Hall, and also the Old South, at an hour
when the Old South people were not worshiping in
it; but shortly after, when it was built, — not the
one you now see, but a wooden building which stood
on the same spot, — the boys of the Latin School
near by broke the windows and daubed the building.
They heard their parents speak angrily of it, and boys
are generally a little more fierce patriots than their
fathers are.   Things went on from bad to worse, and
the chief men thought they saw Boston coming under
the same oppression which their fathers and grandfathers had known in England.   They could not ap-
peal to Parliament, for they had no rights there; they
were subjects of the crown only.   Andros meanwhile
had been traveling through New England, and had
brought all the colonies under his personal rule.   It
looked as if he had accomplished all that the enemies
of New England across the water wished to be done,

and he kept tightening his power. He forbade traveling merchants or peddlers ; every one was to sell only in his own town. The liberty of the towns in choosing their officers was not taken away, but the officers were to act only under instructions from the governor, and only one town-meeting was to be held each year.

" At length the people sent one of their ministers, Increase Mather, to England, to complain of the manner in which they were treated. It was with some difficulty that he got away, but he succeeded in escaping, and once in London he tried, through all manner of influential people, to get a hearing for his oppressed countrymen. Andros, however, was growing more powerful. The king had made him governor of all the English possessions in America, except Pennsylvania, Delaware, Maryland, and Virginia, and he was moving about everywhere strengthening his position. All manner of rumors now began to get about. People in England were very uneasy. They told dark stories about the connection of James, who was now king of England, with France ; and it began to be said in Boston that the king meant to sell all New England to the hated French, and that there were treacherous plans on foot for setting the Indians against the settlements.

" You know a little of English history, and you know that in 1689 William of Orange, at the invitation of English patriots, came to England with an

army, and King James fled without fighting, so that
by a peaceful revolution the Stuart kings were set
aside, and England was governed as it has been ever
since by a Parliament which has the power, and a
royal family which has the name. Well, rumors had
been crossing the Atlantic as to what might happen
in England, and the people who got the news were
on tiptoe of expectation. In those days, you remember, there were no newspapers crowded with news
and telegraphic dispatches, but when a ship came into
Boston harbor the captain and passengers brought
letters and intelligence, some of which was quite old.
While everybody was stirred by what was going on
under Andros, a ship came in and dropped its anchor.
It was the 4th of April, 1689. Among those on board
was a young man named John Winslow, who belonged
in Boston. He had been abroad, and was just coming back when the Declaration of the Prince of
Orange, which he made upon landing in England,
was published. He bought some copies, for he knew
it would be good news to the people of Boston. He
must have said something about the papers, perhaps
showed them, for as soon as he was fairly at home
the governor sent the sheriff for him. He went to
the governor, who asked him why he had not come
straight to him with the news. Winslow replied that
he did not think it was his duty. Then the governor
asked for the papers, and he would not give them.

" ' You are a saucy fellow,' said the governor, and

sent him off with the sheriff to some justices of the peace, who also demanded the papers. Winslow refused to give them up, for he said they kept all the news from the people. Then the justices clapped him into prison. But the news had come, nevertheless, and for a fortnight the town was in a ferment. It was not yet known how William of Orange had been received, and many were cautious, fearing lest the movement should prove a failure, and that then those who had shared in it would fall under the heavy hand of King James. At length one Thursday, when the lecture would bring a good many people to town, — and, I suppose, more than usual, for public excitement brings people together easily, — it began to be whispered about that there were companies of men forming at either end of the town. Ever since early morning people had been astir, and it was known that Governor Andros had gone for safety to Fort Hill. The frigate Rose was in the harbor, but Captain George, commanding it, was on shore. A party of men suddenly appeared, and arrested him. Then about nine o'clock, the beat of a drum was heard, and on the beacon an ensign was run up. The drums continued to beat signals throughout the town, and those who were not in the secret were running hither and thither to see what was done. Parties of men armed went silently about to the houses of officers of the government, and soon the jail doors were opened and Andros's friends were marched in behind the

gates. Then those who were gathered at the Town
House, at the head of State, then King Street, where
the old State House now stands, saw a company march-
ing up the street, led by Captain Hill, and escorting
some grave citizens, who had been magistrates when
the Charter was held, and had kept aloof from Andros and his government. At the head of them was
old Simon Bradstreet, eighty-seven years of age, and
one of the few survivors of the company which had
come over with Winthrop. They marched up the
steps into the Town House and into the Council Chamber. The crowd gathered outside and stayed there
till noon, when the gentlemen who had been in the
Council Chamber appeared on the balcony looking
down King Street, and one of them read aloud a paper which was called a

DECLARATION OF THE GENTLEMEN, MERCHANTS, AND INHABITANTS OF BOSTON, AND THE COUNTRY ADJACENT.

It was a statement of the wrongs they had suffered at
the hands of Andros and ended thus ; " and grandfather went to the shelf, took down a book, and read : —
　" ' We do therefore seize upon the persons of those
few ill men, which have been (next to our sins) the
grand authors of our miseries ; resolving to secure
them for what justice, orders from his Highness, with
the English Parliament shall direct, lest, ere we are
aware, we find (what we may fear being on all sides

in danger) ourselves to be by them given away to a
foreign power, before such orders can reach unto us;
for which orders we now humbly wait. In the mean
time, firmly believing that we have endeavored
nothing but what mere duty to God and our country
calls for at our hands, we commit our enterprise unto
the blessing of Him who hears the cry of the oppressed; and advise all our neighbors, for whom we
have thus ventured ourselves, to join with us in
prayers, and all just actions, for the defense of the
land.' "

"You see," grandfather went on, "it was a pretty
bold thing for these Boston men to do. They had
shut up the king's officers in prison, and taken the
government into their own hands, and it was not yet
known whether or not William of Orange had got
the power in England. The governor was in the
fort, the old citizens were in the Town House, the
frigate was in the harbor, where was also the castle,
and armed men were pouring into Boston from the
country about. It looked as if a fight was imminent.
The governor sent a messenger from the fort to some
of the chief citizens asking for a conference. They
refused, and instead sent a demand to the governor
to give up the fort, or they would attack it. The
captain of the frigate was under guard, but the lieu-
tenant on board got the vessel in fighting order and
made ready to meet an attack. He sent a boat to
bring off Andros, but as soon as the boat landed the

crew were seized by the men who were carrying the
demand to Andros, their arms taken from them, and
the boat detained.   It was now late in the afternoon.
The governor wanted to parley, but his request was
refused, and presently he came out from the fort,
surrendered it, and was marched to the Town House
with his companions.   These were placed in jail, and
the governor sent under a guard to the house of Mr.
Usher, one of the chief merchants in town, and living
very likely where his father had lived close by the
Town House.

"They now had the governor in their power, and
the next day, April 19, they made him sign an order
for the surrender of the castle, and so down to the
castle went the citizen soldiers and took possession.
Then all the guns in the castle and fort, and in the
shipping too in the harbor, were pointed toward the
frigate, which was the only obstacle remaining.   Captain George begged not to be obliged to surrender
his command, and the more cautious were reluctant
to fire upon one of his majesty's ships, which would
have been a serious offense, so they came to a happy
agreement.   The sails of the frigate were brought on
shore and kept carefully, so that the vessel could not
possibly get away, and there the matter rested.

"The Little Revolution had been accomplished,
and the next thing was to have a new government
in place of the one they had overthrown.   The governor and his adherents were in prison; the governor

indeed tried to escape, disguised in woman's clothes, but he was brought back. Joseph Dudley, whom the people hated because they thought he had betrayed them, and whom Andros had made Chief Justice, was not in Boston at the time, but they found him, put him in his house in Roxbury, and set a guard over him, quite as much for his protection against the fury of the people as for any reason. So the men who had been most active formed themselves into a council for the safety of the people and conservation of the peace, and made old Simon Bradstreet president of it. Yet they did not dare do much. They had not been appointed by anybody but themselves, so they sent out to all the towns asking them each to send two delegates to a convention in Boston; Boston however was to have four. These delegates agreed in asking the magistrates, who were in office when the Charter was abrogated and Dudley had his commission, to resume the government under the old Charter, but they refused. Then they asked the council to continue to act as a committee for public safety until they could go back and get fresh instructions from the towns.

"You see, boys, it was the towns that had always governed. The people met in their town-meetings, and chose some of their number to look after the local affairs of the town, and some to go up to Boston and sit in the General Court, just as they do now, to manage, with the delegates from the various towns, the affairs of the whole colony. Andros had put a stop to that. He did not want the people to govern themselves in this way; he chose to govern them himself, and the moment Andros was shut up, all the towns were ready to go on again just as they had before. But the Charter had been declared by the courts of England no longer to exist, and to set up a new government under the old Charter was to act directly against the law. However, the towns again sent delegates to Boston, and out of fifty-four towns, all but fourteen voted to do just this thing; and so when the convention met, after discussing the matter for two days, it was decided to ask the governor and the magistrates, who had been chosen at the last election under the old Charter, to form a General Court, and resume government just as if nothing had happened during the past three or four years."

"And did anybody stop them, grandfather?"

"No. The news came soon that William and Mary were King and Queen of England, and were to be so proclaimed by the old magistrates. Two Bostonians in London — Sir William Phipps and Increase Mather — had fortunately been on hand to prevent mischief, and they succeeded in stopping an order from the king that Sir Edmund Andros was to continue the government until further arrangements could be made."

"And did we keep our Charter after all?"

"No. The old Charter remained in force only till

a new one could be made, and that one differed from the first. There was to be a governor, but he as well as some other officers were to be appointed by the crown. There was to be a General Court chosen by the towns, but the laws which they made were to be approved by the king, and in other ways the colony was more directly under English rule. From 1630 to 1689 the people had really governed themselves, and in that time they had learned how to do it. From this time till 1775 they were to be governed by England, for the benefit of England, but it was not possible for the people to forget self-government as long as there was a town-meeting and a town-church, each under the government of the people of the town. Andros had been gathering all the northern colonies under one government ; under this new Charter a Province was constituted, which embraced Massachusetts, Plymouth, Maine, and Nova Scotia. A Bostonian who was a favorite in England was made the first governor."

"So the Little Revolution was over," said Benjy.

"Yes. There was no blood shed that I know of, and it went on at the same time as the Great Revolution in England, and much in the same way. It was a real revolution though, and when everything was settled, Boston was nearer to London than it had been for some time. After this whatever took place in England was likely to affect Boston, and what went on in Boston was pretty sure to be heard of in London. It had been so before, when the early Puritans were on good terms with the Puritan leaders in England ; but now it was not so much in matters of church and religion and politics that the two were brought together, as it was in business and trade and the connection of families. Boston before had been the chief town of a little self-governing community of religious men. Now it was the principal commercial town of a flourishing English colony. Englishmen were sent over from London to govern it, and governors who came from the court were quite as anxious to please the king as they were to make friends with the people whom they came to govern."

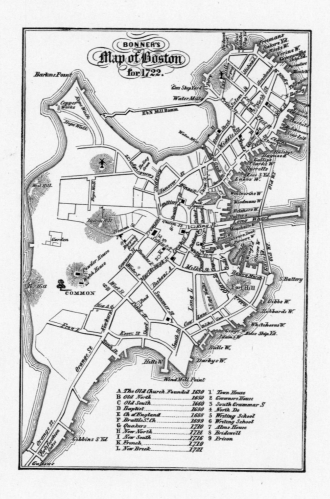

BONNER'S
Map of Boston
for 1722.

Bartons Point

Copper Works

E & N Mill Damm

Cee's Ship Yard
Water Mills

West Hill

Honover St.

Beacon Hill

Garden

Powder House
Watch House

COMMON

Fox Hill

Ward St.

Common St.

Newberry St.

Frog L.

Essex St.

Orange St.

Orange St.
New Boston or water

Gibbins S Yd.

Gallows

Hills W.

Wind Mill Point

Darby's W.

Halls W.

Fort Hill

S. Battery

Gibbs W.

Hubbards W.

Whitehorns W.

Eves Ship Yd.

Long Wharf

Dalton Wharf

A The Old Church Founded 1630	1 Town House
B Old North _____ 1650	2 Governors House
C Old South _____ 1650	3 South Grammar S.
D Baptist _____ 1630	4 North Do.
E Ch. d'England _____ 1688	5 Writing School
F Brattle St. Ch. _____ 1699	6 Writing School
G Quakers _____ 1710	7 Alms House
H New North _____ 1714	8 Bridewell
I New South _____ 1716	9 Prison
K French _____ 1710	
L New Brick _____ 1721	

CHAPTER VII.

BOSTON PIRATES AND TREASURE-HUNTERS.

THOUGH they had lived all their young lives in Boston, the boys had never till now fairly visited the North End. They had been to the Boston and Maine Railroad station, and to the East Boston ferry, but the region lying between these points and stretching to the water side was a *terra incognita* to them. One day grandfather took them with him on a walk. He carried them first upon the outskirts of the district, leading them round the foot of Copp's Hill. They walked by Causeway Street, past the railway stations, and round by Commercial Street. When they came to Charles River Bridge, grandfather told them that once the hill on their right, which now they scarcely saw to be a hill, rose so sharply from the shore as to be climbed with great difficulty.

"It was cut down," he said, " a great many years ago, and used to fill in the land at its base and the beach, which was where this Commercial Street is now. They made a road here by the water, at the foot of the hill, and here were wharves and landing places. The whole high ground above us was called Mill Field, and there stood a windmill almost as soon

as Boston was settled.   The road was really a good
deal higher then, I think, than it is now, and ran
more along the slope of the hill at this point."   They
had been walking quickly. when grandfather began
to look about him, up and down, to stop and glance
up at the houses.

"What are you looking for, grandfather?" asked
Benjy.

"Can either of you boys make out Henchman's
Lane?"

"Why here is Henchman Street," said Jeff, spy-
ing the name on a lamp post.

"To be sure, to be sure; it must be the same
place.   Now let me see," and the old gentleman,
crossing to the foot of the street, looked over the
way at the buildings.

"This used to be a high bank here," he went on,
"falling off toward the water, and just at the foot of
this street, not far from where we are standing, nearly
fifty years ago, if I remember, — I was a young man
then, — they were digging to lay the foundation of
those houses opposite, when they came upon a brick
arch, built under the hill, and they left it there, or
a part of it, at any rate.   I've not been here from
that day to this, and I'd like to see if it's here still."
He struck his cane on the pavement.

"Doesn't it sound hollow, grandfather?" asked
Benjy, cocking his head to one side.

"Tut, tut, child; don't make fun of your old

grandfather. Come, we 'll try that house there."
They crossed the street, and rapped at the door of
a house. A young woman came through the entry
and opened the door wide.

" Good-day," said grandfather, putting on his most
benevolent look, for he was not sure they would be
welcome. " I 've come with my grandchildren on a
hunt for a curious relic that used to be in this neighborhood. When I was a young man, and these
houses were built, I remember the workmen came
upon a brick arch under ground, and I 'm told it is
still to be seen, leading out of a cellar. Did you
ever see it in your house ? "

" Well," she said, " I did hear once something
about it, but I never saw it. Come in, sir, and I 'll
speak to father." So in they went, and followed
their guide to a large room at the end of the house.
There sat the mother over her child's cradle, and the
father by the cooking stove, eating a bit, while a
canary and a mocking-bird and an Irish blackbird
hung in cages and twittered. Grandfather and the
boys stood in the middle of the room.

" There 's a gentleman come to ask something about
an old arch, father," said the young woman.

" I hope I 'm not intruding," said grandfather, politely, " but I take my grandchildren out to walk
sometimes to see old Boston, and as I came by here
I remembered an old brick archway or cave that was
found about this spot some fifty years ago or so. Is
there anything of the kind in your cellar ? "

"There's a sort of coal hole there," said the man. "I've never used it; you can see it, if you want to."

"Thank you; if it's no trouble, I should like to very much."

"No trouble at all," and getting up the man lighted a lamp and led them to the cellar stairs. "Have a care," said he; "the passage is dark." They stumbled along behind him, and presently came to an underground room, lighted by cellar windows looking out on the street. In the corner was a great collection of heavy blocks for hoisting hung upon stout sticks. The man pulled them off one by one, and threw them into a heap on the cellar floor; then he drew aside some boards which rested against the outer wall, and they began to make out an opening. The boys grew very much excited.

"I see a hole!" cried Jeff.

"It's the place, you may be sure," said Benjy, and, as board after board was removed, the opening grew larger. The man went forward with his lamp, and the others, stooping, followed him through the square opening into an arched chamber, where they could not stand upright. It was about four feet from the ground to the top of the brick arch, and the floor measured about twelve feet by ten. At the further end was a solid stone wall, and the wall through which the opening was pierced was also of stone, being the foundation of the house.

"This certainly is the place," said grandfather.

" What do you suppose it was ?" asked Jeff of the owner of the house.

" Well, I never heard. I 've thought of using it for coal, but I never put any in here."

" Here 's an iron pipe," said Benjy, taking hold of one which ran across the top of the arch. " Is it a water-pipe ? "

" No, it 's an old pipe. The water-pipes are farther out and lower down. What do you think this cave was, sir ? " he asked of grandfather.

" There were a good many stories about it when it was first discovered at the cutting down of the hill," said grandfather. " We only see a part of it. The opening was toward the water, and I suspect it ran in farther than this stone wall, but that when they came to lay the sewer they stoned it up. At first it was thought to be a smuggler's cave."

" Oh, jolly !" said Jeff. " And look here, grandfather ; just see this brick box." The man who lived in the house went over to the side where Jeff had found what he called his brick box. He felt about it but could find no opening. It was like a brick column projecting above the earth about fifteen inches.

" I must pry this open some time," said he.

" Perhaps the smugglers buried some money in it," said Jeff.

" Doubloons," said Benjy ; " they always buried doubloons."

" But it was not a smuggler's cave," said grandfather. " It was proved to be a store chamber built by one Captain Gruchy in the wars with the French. He was probably a privateer, and stowed away here the goods which he captured from the enemy. Gruchy owned this side of the hill, and built a wharf below here by sinking two vessels which he had captured. But they must have rotted away long ago."

" Any way," said Jeff, " it's just the place for smugglers."

" Yes," said grandfather, as they crawled out of the opening into the cellar again ; " and it was very likely used for purposes something like it. It is said there were other caves built like this, where people used to hide goods to keep them out of the custom-house officers' way during the time when Andros was governor. Randolph was the first customs officer, and he was Andros's right hand man. He was a pretty zealous officer, and the Boston people hated him." They went up stairs again, and dusted each other carefully, for they were pretty well covered with cobwebs.

" Well, did you find it ? " asked the good-natured mother, who was still by the cradle.

" Yes, indeed, and a queer place it is. We are very much obliged to you," turning to the man, " for showing it to us."

" Not at all, I haven't been there myself for a good many years, and I've lived here for twenty years."

" You didn't know that you had a historical mu-

seum here, did you ?" said grandfather good-nat-
uredly.

"No, I might set up a show."

"Only dig into that brick box," said Jeff, as they
went **away** ; "I should n't wonder at all if it was full
of — full of " —

"Oh, say diamonds," said Benjy. "We might as
well, as long as we don't know anything about it."

"People always want to pick up riches," said
grandfather, as they walked up Henchman Street,
"but it generally happens that for one person who
makes a lucky hit, there are ninety-nine who waste
their time hunting, and might have got their riches
by good, honest industry. Now there was Daniel
Henchman, from whom this street was named. He
was a Boston man, and in his younger days was an
assistant master at your Latin School. He was a
captain in the militia, and in King Philip's war took
a company of Boston soldiers out of town. He was
a good citizen, and attended to his work. I don't
believe he ever hunted for treasure, but here on
Charter Street, at the corner of Salem Street, was
where Sir William Phips lived, and he was a great
treasure-hunter; and though he came to be governor of Massachusetts, he is remembered best by
how he found some treasure, and how he lost Quebec.
We will walk home now, and I'll tell you about him
on the way."

"How came Phips to be Sir William, grandfather,
if he was born in America?"

"America was part of the British Empire then, Benjy, and the king could make a knight of a Boston man if he chose. Phips was not born in Boston. He was born in Maine, on the Kennebec, at what was then a frontier settlement, and grew up there poor and ignorant, for his mother and father are said to have had twenty-six children, and living there in the wilderness I don't think there was much chance for the boy to grow either rich or learned. But he was ambitious, and not meaning to stay in the backwoods learned the trade of ship-carpentry, and that brought him to Boston while he was still a young man. He married a widow with money, and learned to read and write indifferently well. At that time there were a great many pirates and rovers on the seas, and all sorts of stories were told about the West Indies. Boston vessels carried on a trade with that part of the country, and I suppose that the islands and Spanish Main seemed to those accustomed to bleak New England very rich and prosperous. Then the Spaniards were still thought of as the owners of gold and silver mines in Mexico and South America, and Spanish ships were supposed to be laden with treasures. The pirates always made for these ships as best worth capturing. The sailors and ship-carpenters told wonderful stories, and Phips heard of a Spanish vessel which had been wrecked off the Bahamas. He was owner and master of a small craft, and he made a voyage to find it. Sure enough there was the wreck, and he managed to pick a few things up, though not enough to pay for the trouble. But he heard of another and more important galleon which had been sunk near Port de la Plata, more than fifty years before.

" So he went home with his head full of this sunken treasure. People were as eager then to get rich fast in this way as nowadays they are to find a silver or gold mine. He had not enough money, however, to enable him to fit out an expedition, and he went to England to see if he could get the English government to send him out. I do not believe he said much about his plans in Boston, and if he did he was laughed at; but strange to say he did succeed in persuading the king to put him in command of the Rose-Algier, a ship carrying eighteen guns and ninety-five men. Some people think that this enterprising and uneducated ship-carpenter went directly to the king, and told him such stories in his blunt way as made him think Phips really would bring back vast treasures ; and then everybody, from the king down, had faith in the stories of fabulous wealth brought away from Mexico by the Spaniards.

" Phips did not get the treasure, but he showed himself a man of real grit, and his adventures on this voyage are worth telling, for they help to explain how such a man in a time when book learning was even more esteemed than now in New England should have come to be governor. The crew who had shipped on the Rose-Algier were easily obtained, for they were as eager to pick up money from the bottom of the ocean as Phips was, but they were a wild set, and not the kind to bear disappointment with patience. So when they failed to find the place, after fishing about, they demanded that the ship should become a piratical craft and they should be led against the Spanish vessels that were cruising in those waters. Phips refused, and an open mutiny broke out which he put down courageously. But the crew grew more and more determined to have their own way, and at length an opportunity came which they nearly secured. The ship was out of repair, and in order to get at her copper bottom, Phips took her to a small and uninhabited island, and anchoring her in a cove, moved on to the island a great part of her stores, and disposed of the rest so that she should careen over. He stretched a bridge across from the ship to a rocky projection of the island, and made an encampment near by, covering the stores. The crew got permission to go off into the interior of the island and all except seven or eight, who stayed with Phips and were at work with him, went into the woods out of sight and hearing. There they held a consultation and determined to go back to the ship at night-fall, seize Phips and the others on the vessel, bind them, leave them on the island, and putting the stores back to set sail as pirates. In talking it over, however, they found they should need with them a

certain carpenter who was then at work on the ship ;
so they sent for him on some pretense, told him what
they intended, and threatened to kill him instantly if
he would not join them. He begged for leave first
to go back to the ship and get his tools, and they let
him go, but sent two or three to keep watch and see
that he did not betray them. After he had been on
board the vessel a little while he pretended to be
taken suddenly sick and went to the cabin to get
some medicine. There he had for a single moment
a chance to tell Phips of the plot. The captain bade
him go back and join the crew as if nothing had happened, and back went the carpenter with the other
seamen to shore.

" There only remained two hours before the mutineers were to strike, and Phips made instant preparations to meet them. He found the half dozen with
him ready to stand by him. There were a few of
the ship's guns which had been removed to the island
to protect the stores in case the island had been
inhabited. There was not time to get these aboard,
and if they had attempted it, they would surely have
shown what they were about, but as men were going
back and forth across the little bridge, it was not
difficult to withdraw the charges from the guns, and
to bring back all the ammunition from the island.
Then Phips loaded all the guns on the ship, and
trained them to cover the encampment, drew the
bridge in, and was now ready for the mutineers. As

soon as they came within hearing he called out to
them that he should fire upon them if they went near
the stores, and made them stay at a distance. Then
he put out his bridge again and set two or three of
his faithful men at work bringing off to the ship the
stores that were on the island, and told the mutineers
that he was going to do to them just what they had
determined to do to him ; he was going to leave them
on the island to starve. That brought them to their
senses, and they began to beg to be taken back.
They declared they had nothing against him except
that he would not turn pirate with them, and promised to obey him, if he would take them back again.
So he made them give up all their arms, and by
keeping watch over them, he managed to get to
Jamaica without further danger, and there he discharged the disaffected crew and took on another."

"But did n't he find the treasure ?"

"He did not know exactly where to look for it,
Jeff ; that was the trouble, and he tried to find some
one who could guide him to the spot. At length he
came upon an old Spaniard at the island of Hayti,
who showed him the very reef where the wreck had
been sunk. But look as hard as he could Phips could
make out nothing; and as the Rose-Algier was still
out of repair and not thoroughly manned, he was
obliged to go back to England without the treasure.

"You would have thought that that would be the
end, but it was not. Captain Phips had shown him-

self so brave a man, and besides had become so pos-
itive that he now knew the exact spot where to dive
for his treasure, that while the government would
not give him another vessel, he was able to persuade
the Duke of Albemarle and a few other gentlemen
to help him form another expedition. He knew better what he wanted in the way of equipment, and
now thoroughly prepared, off he set for Port de la
Plata again. Here he anchored his ship in the harbor, and prepared for the search. He could not get
near enough to the reef with the ship, so he built a
stout boat, and went to work himself with his adze as
in the old days when he was only a ship-carpenter.
Then he had, besides, a small vessel, and he sent
this vessel and boat out, placing on board some men
whom he could trust, and also some Indians who were
used to diving for sponges or for treasures. Phips
himself remained with the ship.

" When the men came to the reef they put out in
their boat, and were able to come close to it. It was
under water, but close to the surface in places. Then
again it would fall off suddenly and in a very steep
fashion. The water was so clear and still that they
could see very distinctly. The divers plunged down,
too, but brought back nothing. The men leaned
over the side of the boat, and peered down through
the transparent water. They knew that if they
found the treasure a part would belong to them. But
they could make out nothing, and were just going to

give up the search, when one of the men spied a curious piece of sea-weed in the crevice of a rock. He sent down a diver to bring it up, and when the diver came back, he declared that he had found some cannon lying close by it. Immediately the men were in the water, for they were sure they had found now the sunken ship. Down they went, and when they appeared again, one of the divers had brought up a great mass of silver. They marked the spot with a buoy, put back to the tender, and made all haste to report to Phips.

" He would not believe their story at first, he had so often been disappointed ; but when they showed him the silver, he cried, ' Thanks be to God, we are all made ; ' and no time was lost in getting to work. Everybody was ready to do his best, and in a few days they had fished up treasure to the value of three hundred thousand pounds ; part was in coin, part in uncoined gold and silver, and part in precious stones. The coins were in bags, which had lain there at the bottom of the ocean for fifty years, and were covered with shells and lime so thickly that they had to break into them with iron tools ; but as soon as they had made a breach, out poured the gold coin. The men were full of excitement, and one poor fellow, a ship-master who happened to be in those waters, and was invited by Phips to join him, actually went mad over his good fortune, so it was not such very good fortune after all. They had not finished their work when their provisions gave out, and even gold and silver would be of no use to them if they had no food."

"Don't you remember," broke in Benjy eagerly, "how Robinson Crusoe found some gold and silver on his wreck, and said, ' O drug ! what art thou good for ? ' "

"Yes," said Jeff dryly ; "and how, upon second thoughts, he took it away." Grandfather laughed.

"Robinson was a wise man. Gold and silver are not to be despised, though they will do nothing for a man unless there is somebody else to take them in exchange ; and Phips and his men found the gold and silver very useful when they went into port again. They tried to keep the matter secret, so that they might go back and get some more, but Adderley, the poor fellow who went mad afterward, and whom they left there, was not careful to keep the secret; it leaked out, others went there from the neighborhood, and Phips never got any more. He had a good cargo of gold and silver, however, and with this he set sail for England. Here he was received warmly by the Duke of Albemarle and his friends, to whom most of the treasure belonged, because they had been at the expense of getting it. Phips himself got but sixteen thousand pounds in all, but that was a fortune for him, and then the Duke of Albemarle made a present to Mrs. Phips of a gold cup worth a thousand pounds more, and moreover King James knighted the

8

captain, and he was now Sir William Phips, and a very famous man indeed.

" His riches and his title did not make him at once a wise or a very cultivated person. He could write little better than when he first began to learn a few years before, and he was a rough-spoken, hot-headed ship-carpenter and sailor. Yet he loved New England and Boston, and he refused to stay in England where King James wanted him, but went back to Boston. For a time he was a man of singular consequence, since he was befriended by King James, and at the same time he was a friend of Boston, so that he had it in his power to help Boston just when the town needed it, for he came back only a little while before the Little Revolution, of which I have told you, broke out. But he was not fitted to get along very well with people, and back he went to England, where he arrived just after James had fled, and William and Mary were on the throne. James, you know, had not given up his claims to the throne of England, and he still had many adherents. He tried to persuade Sir William Phips to go back to Boston, and be governor under him; but Phips knew Boston better than that, and, instead of casting in his fortunes with James, he stayed in London and did all he could to help New England get the Charter she so much wanted.

" I will not try to follow the ship-carpenter through his life. He came back to Boston, and headed an expedition to Nova Scotia, which captured Port Royal, and that is the reason why, when a new province of New England was made, Nova Scotia was included. Boston was highly elated that her little naval expedition should have been so successful, and nothing would do but they must drive the French out of the country altogether, and so a most foolhardy attempt was made, under Sir William Phips, to take Quebec, the strongest fortified place on the continent. The expedition had a most dismal failure, but Phips, when he came home, did all he could to make up the losses which were caused by it. He was a restless man, and he had great schemes for taking Canada by other means, and went over to England to persuade the king to it; but King William was too busy with other matters. However, he liked this bluff sailor, and finally, when the new Charter was given to New England, he sent over Sir William Phips as the first governor under it. The new governor had had so much to do with getting the Charter, with Increase Mather, a notable Boston minister, that the town changed the name of Green Lane, where Phips lived, to Charter Street, and by that name it has gone ever since.

" He was governor only a little over two years and got himself into a good deal of trouble, for he was a quick-tempered man, and though he had much shrewdness and resolution he was ignorant and made a good many mistakes. He died finally in 1695, only forty-four years old, and when he was dead people forgot his mistakes and remembered chiefly his generosity and honesty."

" Grandfather, what became of his wife's gold cup ? " asked Benjy.

" I don't know that I ever heard."

" Perhaps it is buried in the brick box," suggested Jeff. " The land there belonged to Phips, did n't it ? "

" Yes, it was part of his place, and Captain Gruchy bought his house with the land down to the water's edge, and lived there."

" Well, I mean to believe it," said Jeff. " It 's there, you may be sure. Don't you believe some of Captain Kidd's money is buried somewhere, grandfather ? "

" I have no doubt a good deal of Captain Kidd's money got well taken care of. He lived, you know, when Phips was living."

" Why, I did not know that."

" Oh yes, and what is very interesting, the Earl of Bellomont, who succeeded Sir William Phips as governor of New England, made a contract with Captain Kidd to put down piracy."

" Set a thief to catch a thief," said Jeff.

" It does look like it ; but it is really very difficult to say just who the thieves were at this time. The seas were full of rovers who fell upon merchant ships, as highway robbers took purses on the roads, and just

as some of the highway robbers appeared to be inno-
cent farmers when they were not robbing people, so
the pirates sometimes appeared to be trading vessels.
Then, too, there was no such navy in the English
service at home or abroad as could keep order on the
high seas, and there were long lines of coast without
towns and not very well known, where the pirates
could hide. It was as if a man was going through a
piece of dark woods when he was sailing a vessel to
the Gulf of Mexico ; a robber might jump out of the
bushes suddenly, and a pirate might dart out from
behind an island or projecting cape. Besides all this,
wars were breaking out every little while in Europe,
and when that happened any one was thought to do
a good thing who fitted out a vessel to catch and
plunder one of the enemy's ships, and it was very
easy when the war was over for privateers to keep
on catching and plundering, and that was what these
pirates did.

" Now Boston was a commercial town, and it was
by its ships and trade that it was growing rich. The
merchants could not have pirates catching their ships,
and what made them very angry was that they were
pretty sure that some of their neighbors were quietly
fitting out pirate ships and sending them off after
their vessels. Everything of this kind was of course
kept very secret, so that it is not possible now to
know exactly what was done, but we know that they
passed severe laws against piracy, and when they

caught a pirate they hung him.   You know Nix's
Mate in the harbor ? "

"Oh yes," said the boys.

"Well, the Boston people had a gibbet there on
that lonely place; common pirates who had been

hung they buried there in the
sand, but the captain and ring-
leaders they hung up in irons
from the gibbet, so that when
sailors came into port, they
could see the skeleton and take
warning."

Nix's Mate.

"But tell us about Captain Kidd," said Jeff.

"Captain Kidd was a New York man, and Lord
Bellomont, with a number of other people, furnished
money to fit out an expedition to catch pirates, with
Kidd to take charge of it.   Just as the Duke of Albemarle had supplied Captain Phips with a vessel to
fish up treasure from the sunken wreck, so Lord
Bellomont employed Kidd, and all who were interested in the venture were to divide between themselves all the profits, giving the king a tenth part, for
they would hang the pirates and divide the pirates'
booty."

"But I should think the people whom the pirates
plundered ought to have their goods back again,"
said Benjy.

"I am afraid they would not get much.   The earl
and those who paid for Captain Kidd's services would

claim all he captured, and not trouble themselves to hunt up the unfortunate owners. But it did not prove to be very profitable business, certainly not to Captain Kidd, who was finally hung, nor to the Earl of Bellomont, who was always obliged to defend himself against evil charges. Kidd sailed away to the East Indies, and after a while rumors came that, instead of capturing pirates, he had turned pirate himself. There was one ship in particular, called the Quedah Merchant, which he was said to have taken, and, as the owners were not at war with England, they demanded the arrest of Kidd, and the English government sent out orders to all the colonies to have him arrested when he should appear. By and by he was heard of on the coast. Then he was found distributing treasure along the shores of Long Island Sound, and at length he established himself at Gardiner's Island, and sent word to Bellomont where he was, and that if he might have a safe conduct to Boston, he would come on and prove his innocence. He had captured the Quedah Merchant, to be sure, and had her safe in a creek by the island of Hayti, but he would explain all that when he came to Boston.

" Bellomont was a partner of Kidd the pirate-catcher, but he was a royal governor, and it would hardly do to make terms with Kidd the pirate. He laid Kidd's proposition before his council, and by their advice wrote to Kidd telling him he might come to Boston, where he would be fitted out to go after the Quedah, and nobody should harm him or touch his treasure until orders should come from England, always provided he was telling the truth. So Kidd came to Boston, and with him came Mr. Livingstone, who also was interested in the venture. The captain was bidden bring in a full narrative of his adventures, which he had said would prove his innocence ; lists of his men, both those who were faithful and those who he said had deserted him because he would not turn pirate ; and a full account also of the treasure which he had brought, and that which he had left aboard the Quedah. He was to have it ready the next day by five o'clock. He came at the time appointed, but excused himself as he had not yet had time to make up his accounts. So another day was given him, and he did not appear ; he was sent for, but when he came he made a fresh excuse. Then, when he left, the governor showed the council letters which he had received from England, ordering the arrest of Kidd and seizure of his goods. It is impossible to say whether these orders had really just come or had been held back by the governor until he had taken alarm. At any rate, Kidd was arrested. He had been threatening, through Livingstone, not to give up the Quedah until Bellomont had surrendered a bond for ten thousand pounds, which Kidd had given him. Now he began to beg the governor to let him go back to Hayti, under guard as a prisoner, and bring off the ship with its rich cargo. It looks a little like a bribe, and I rather think that Bellomont's refusal indicates that he was ready to act honorably. Kidd did not go after it, and nobody knows what became of the Quedah. Its mysterious disappearance gave rise to a great many of the stories which have sprung up of the burying of Kidd's treasures. Twenty years later another pirate named Bellamy was wrecked off the coast of Cape Cod. His ship, which was broken to pieces, was called the Whidah, and, though the two words are spelled differently, Whidah is pronounced somewhat as Quedah would be by the Spaniards, and it is not impossible that it was Kidd's ship put to piratical uses."

" But, grandfather, where had it been for twenty years ? "

" Oh, I don't know ; but it is not at all likely that it had been staying in that Hayti creek. Possibly the men left behind had got tired of waiting for Kidd, and had gone off on their own account, but had for a time kept their movements secret. It would be like such a pirate as Bellamy, if he came into possession of the Quedah, to keep the name as a boast."

" And what became of Kidd ? "

" He was taken finally to England, tried for murder and piracy, and hung on the former charge. Some of the Boston men were very unwilling to have him taken away for trial ; they did not like the principle ; they thought that offenses against law in Amer-

ica should be tried in America. But they were over-
ruled. Captain Kidd was not the last of the pirates,
but the mystery about the Quedah, and the confu-
sion about his connection with men high in authority, have made him one of the most famous."

"I suppose your father never saw Captain Kidd,
grandfather?"

"No, my boy, nor my grandfather, but my great-
grandfather might easily have seen him, for he was
twenty-seven years old when Kidd was in Boston."

"And he was" —

"Atavus, Jeff, atavus."

"Next comes abavus, grandfather. Why, we're
getting down among your relations."

"Aye, Jeff, I can just remember abavus, my grandfather. He was born in 1717, and was ninety-five
when he died."

CHAPTER VIII.

THE PROVINCE HOUSE.

It happened that grandfather had a plaster cast which needed repairing, and so he had an errand one day to Garey's, in Province-House Court. The boys went with him, going down Montgomery Place and by the stone steps which led to Province Street, and so by that narrow passage to the court where were various small shops, — gold-beaters and shoemakers and tailors. They had often been there, and it was no new thing for them to go into Mr. Garey's shop, and ring the bell by opening the door. They liked to walk about among the white plaster images, to see the swarthy foreigners at work, and to apply their small classical knowledge to the various statues and busts which they found there. They knew the way also by the little covered passage into Washington Street, and they had read Hawthorne's stories, so they knew what the old Province House was.

" I never thought before," said Jeff, as they walked home that day, " how near the Province House must have been to everything. Why, it was quite in the centre of the town."

" Yes, for a long time it was very near the geographical centre, about half way between the fortification on the Neck and Copp's Hill. It was almost directly opposite the Old South, and the house in which Governor Winthrop lived and died. It was but a little way from the Town Hall and from the dock and the wharves, and all about it were the houses of the rich Boston merchants."

" Was the court where Garey's is the place where the house stood ? " asked Benjy.

" No, that was I suppose part of the garden and open space which used to be about the house. When the house was built it had a lawn in front reaching to Washington Street, with oak-trees, and a gateway upon the street, while two porters' lodges were at either end of the fence. In the early part of this century, the lawn was built over by a block of stores, shutting out the front view, and it was then very likely that the buildings on the side where Mr. Garey's shop is were put up, leaving the court only to give access at the side, and behind the block of stores on Washington Street. The building itself was changed from time to time until 1864, when it was burned, and now all that remains is a portion of the brick walls."

" I don't think I know why it was called Province House," said Benjy.

" Why, just as we say State House now," said Jeff. " The Province House is where the laws were made when Massachusetts was a Province."

" You are nearly right, Jeff. Massachusetts was first a colony ; then, when the old Charter was taken away and a new one given, it was part of the Province of New England ; then, when the Revolution followed, it became the State of Massachusetts. All along, the town of Boston was the chief town of the Colony, then of the Province, and

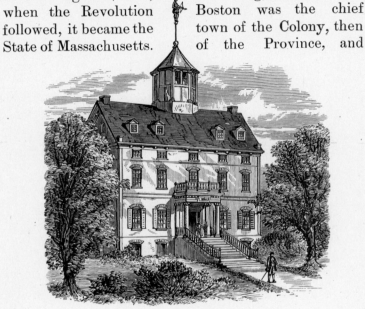

The Old Province House

finally of the State. The Boston town business was transacted at first in the meeting-house, then in the Town House, where the Old State House stands. When the old Town House was burned, in 1711, another of brick was built which lasted till 1747, when the present building was built and continued to be called the Town House. It was here that the meetings of the legislature were held, when Massachusetts was a Colony, when she was part of the Province, and after she became a State. Then it began to be called the State House, and got the name Old State House when the new one on Beacon Hill was built. But the Province House was the residence of the governor, and while the legislature did not meet there and pass laws, there was a good deal of business transacted in it by the governor and his council. It was bought by the province for the governor's residence in 1716. It was built by Peter Sergeant, a Boston merchant, in 1679. Peter married the widow of Sir William Phips. He was a rich man, and he built a house as other rich men did, with a great deal of costly wood-work and tapestry hangings. On the first floor was a great reception room, where the governor stood in full court-dress and received his guests. A broad flight of stone steps led up to the front door, and over it was a portico from which proclamations were read. There was a cupola at the top, from which one could look out over the country, and far away to sea. Perched up on top of the cupola was a copper Indian with glass eyes, and a bow and arrow all ready to shoot. If he had shot anything, it would always have been against the wind, for the Indian was a weather-cock. Behind, where Province Street now is, were the stables attached to the place."

" I wish our governor had a house in Boston which belonged to the State," said Jeff.

" There was some talk before the Old Hancock House on Beacon Hill was taken down of buying that for a governor's residence, but it was not done. People are more indifferent now than they once were to the style in which a governor or any other person of authority lives. In the days when the Province House was occupied by royal governors, there was a great distinction kept up between the governor and those about him, and the common people of Boston. You see the governor was a representative of the king of England ; he governed here in his stead, and the king of England lived in a palace and had many servants who were very respectful toward him. Kings had not then, so much as now, come to intrust the government of their kingdoms to the people themselves meeting in Parliament, and the people had less opportunity for bettering themselves than they now have, so that the distance between the king and people was wider than it is to-day ; the king was higher up and the people lower down. In Boston the difference between the governor and the common people was not so great as it was in England between the king and the peasantry, because a hundred years of self-government had given self-respect and dignity to the people ; they had discussed public affairs in town-meeting, and one and another, by industry and wit, had gained fortune and power. Still there was a difference, and it was shown in the various ways that people like to use for making it seem that they are of more consequence than their neighbors. The governor dressed as a gentleman, who could wear the finest clothes without being in danger of soiling them. The dress of gentlemen was in marked contrast to that of workmen. It is only of late years that people have saved their best clothes to wear at evening parties or on state occasions. You don't see a gentleman nowadays walking about the streets in the morning in a dress coat and white necktie; but if you had lived in provincial Boston, you would have seen the governor and the people of leisure dressed in the most elaborate fashion. There was a famous Boston painter who was living here not far from our house; his name was John Singleton Copley, and he painted a good many portraits of the rich men of the Province. I have a photograph of one of them which I will show you, for it is the portrait of a governor, and you can see how it looked."

They had reached the house by this time, and after tea grandfather got out a portfolio, and showed them the photograph of which he had spoken.

" The photograph has no color, so it does not look as rich as it might, but you can make out something of how the painting looks. He wears a powdered wig, you see, and his hair is crêped at the ears. His coat is of dark blue, and lined with white satin. See how large the sleeves are, and they have very deep cuffs. The waistcoat is of white satin. The picture only gives the upper part. If we could see his legs we should probably find them incased in silk stockings, and silver buckles on the shoes."

" What a long time it must have taken him to dress!" said Jeff.

" To be sure. That was an important part of the day's duty; but then dress made up some of his dignity and position, and he had no daily newspaper to read. When he went out to walk he buckled on a sword, and put a cocked hat on his head. But he more often went in his coach or on horseback, with a negro attendant."

" And were all the royal governors lords and so forth ? " asked Benjy.

" Oh no; they were generally of English families in favor with the king, and they often engaged in business in Boston, taking ventures in ships, just as we saw the Earl of Bellomont in partnership with Captain Kidd. Boston was a busy town, and its business was chiefly in building and sending out ships. Why, Bellomont said in 1698 that there were more good vessels belonging to the town of Boston than to all Scotland and Ireland. The vessels sailed to the West Indies and to England and back. They carried out beef and pork, fish, lumber, and whale oil ; and brought back rice, pitch, spices, logwood, rum, and sugar from the West Indies, and all manner of luxuries from England, — most of the cloth that men and women wore, except the very coarse goods which were spun here. Have n't you sometimes

9

seen signs over stores reading, ' W. I. Goods and Groceries ? ' "

" Why, of course," said both the boys. " We call them Wild Indian goods."

" Well, I suppose that is the way signs read a hundred and fifty years ago, for then all those spices and the sugar and rice which now we get largely from the South, came from the West Indies, especially from the English settlements there, and were classed together under the name West India goods. All along the edge of the town were ship-yards where ships were built, and there were a number of rope-walks where rope was spun. The merchants grew rich and built large and spacious houses for themselves, but these houses were not in great blocks as you see them now. They were sometimes of wood, sometimes of brick, and rarely of stone, and had great gardens about them. You can see such places still at Salem, and indeed I suppose some of the streets there now, like Chestnut, for instance, look very much as Boston streets must have looked a hundred and fifty years ago. You are too young, but your mother remembers very well how Summer Street used to look before stores were built there, and what large trees stood all about that part of town."

"Like those in Essex Street, grandfather ? "

" Yes, very much like those. The houses on Purchase Street, and along the water, had cupolas to give long views across the harbor, and there were summer-houses in the gardens. There was a famous place called the Gardiner Greene place, where Pemberton Square is now, but the hill was higher then, and the garden sloped down to Tremont Row. Then, along the Common, on the eastern side of Tremont Street, near Winter, were other large houses with gardens."

" But where were the shops, grandfather ? "

" They were along Washington Street and up Cornhill. Many of the shopkeepers lived above their shops. The old store, at the corner of Washington and School streets, shows you how the buildings looked then, and I suppose this was one of the larger and better sort. The business centred about the Town Hall and Market Place, and down King Street, or State Street, as it is now called, to the water, and about the Town Dock, where Dock Square is. The merchants used to walk about at noon near the Town House, to transact their business with each other; and they said they were on 'Change, that is, walking in the Exchange, for in London merchants walked in the Royal Exchange, and Boston merchants liked to have the same names as those used in London. You can see a reminiscence of it in Exchange Alley and Exchange Street and Exchange Place. There were coffee-houses, too, just as in London, and here they met to hear the news, and the stages used to start from them. It is not a long while since Young's Hotel was known as Young's Coffee House.

You see vessels were constantly coming and going between London and Boston, and people were passing between the two places, and the Boston people followed the London fashion whenever they could."

" Did they have any Common ? "

"To be sure they did.   As far back as Winthrop's time the Common, with very much the same boundaries as at present, was reserved for the use of the town forever, and it is the one part of Boston which has changed least.   The land lies now very much as then.   There are the same little hills, but of course the paths differ, and the growth of trees and grass is richer.   For a long time people pastured their cows there.   My father did with others.   People used to get stones from it to make their cellar walls with.   You must not think of it in the early days as the trimly kept place which it now is.   Wild roses grew on the hill-sides; there were marshes and wet places, and only two or three trees, for it was a barren and rocky pasture.   The first trees were planted about 1725, along Tremont Street Mall, as far as West Street.   That was called the Great Mall, and people used to walk there for amusement at sundown. The Frog Pond was there, but not walled in, and two other small, low ponds, which have since been filled in.   Where the Soldiers' Monument now is stood a flag-staff, and the place was called Flag-staff Hill.   It was not till the beginning of this century, and within my recollection, that the trees were set out which

BEACON STREET MALL, BOSTON COMMON

border the Beacon Street Mall. The water came up in the Back Bay near to where Charles Street now runs, and there was a boat-house there when I was a boy. In the last century there were rope-walks perched on piles in the marshy tract where the Public Garden is. Opposite Joy Street, on the Beacon Street Mall, was a Wishing Stone, and the young people used to walk round it nine times, and then stand on it or sit down on it and wish their wishes, but they were not to tell their wishes, else they would not come true, just as it is with your wish-bone."

" I wonder," said Jeff, " if the boys had base-ball on the parade ground, and if they had training there ? "

" I 've no doubt they played ball on the Common, and coasted down the hills in winter, just as they rambled over it for berries in the summer time, but base-ball had not been invented then. They had a parade ground, however, not where the present is, for that was a marshy tract filled in by leveling Fox Hill, which stood about half way between Beacon and Boylston streets : no, the parade ground lay, I think, between Tremont Street and the Old Elm. The Old Elm was in all probability standing there then. Do you remember it, Benjy ? "

" I can just remember when it was blown down in a great gale, grandfather."

" Yes, that was in 1876, and now there is a shoot of the old tree growing within the little inclosure

where the old tree stood. If it lives and grows to
be over two hundred years old, the young people in
those days will tell stories about the tree from which
it sprang, and how their grandfathers, farther back
than they can easily count, found it on Boston Common. The Ancient and Honorable Artillery Com-

The Old Elm.

pany used to come out under the tree and parade
and drill, and fire at a mark. Judge Sewall was
captain at one time, and he tells us he made such
poor shots that he fined himself by buying a silver
cup and giving it to the best shot."

"I suppose they were getting ready for the Revolutionary War," said Jeff.

" Yes, though they did not **know it,** and though

the men whom Judge Sewall marched up and down would all be dead before that came : their children and grandchildren were to fight in that war, but the colony and the province were to have much practice in fighting before the Revolution. In the colonial times they were in dread of the Indians, and you remember I told you that Daniel Henchman led a Boston company out in King Philip's war; but after the colonial days, when Massachusetts was part of the province, and Boston was the capital, when governors sent over from England were ruling in the Province House, there were wars with the French. The English and French for a long, long time were hardly ever at peace with each other; and since both England and France had colonies in America, the Englishmen and Frenchmen on this side of the water kept up the quarrel which was going on in Europe. In Europe, indeed, only a narrow channel separated the two countries, and here between the French in Canada and the English in Maine a wilderness intervened, with only a few solitary settlements here and there; but, for all that, a deadly conflict was going on between the two nations, and whenever a peace was made in Europe something was done about the possessions in America, a piece given to the victorious country, or a fort which had been taken was given back. Whenever there was war the people in Boston, who had ships and fishing smacks out, were in fear lest these should be captured by French privateers;

and they thought it would be a fine thing to send a fleet and an army to take the French possessions in the North. Besides, the French made friends with the Indians more easily than the English did, and so when there was war, the Indians helped the French, and that embittered the English still more.

" Now the governor in Province House was governor over all the province, and so when there was war between France and England, he was the one on this side of the water who made the arrangements for such fighting as was done here, and if he was a military man, as he was more than once, he would find life in Boston rather dull, and would care most to be fitting out fleets and sending out little armies to the north and east where the French were established. The Boston men thought it would be a fine thing if they could capture the forts and hold the harbors there. Then they could fish without fear, and they could show the people in Great Britain that they were Englishmen, too, who were zealous for the English name.

" There were five notable excursions made by Boston men against the French, and I will tell you briefly what they were. The Boston merchants had been greatly annoyed by French cruisers which ran out from a little fortified harbor in Nova Scotia, or Acadia as it was then called, and an expedition was fitted out from Boston in 1690 against this harbor of Port Royal. It was placed under the command of

Sir William Phips, who sailed with seven vessels, manned by two hundred and eighty-five men, and carrying from four to five hundred militia-men. They found no cruisers in the harbor, and the fort was defended by about seventy soldiers only, and unprepared for standing an attack or a siege, so the commander surrendered, and was carried off to Boston. Phips easily got control of the other settlements, but he made no provision for a permanent government, and after he was gone the French slipped back again. He and his men plundered Port Royal, and robbed the poor commander of pretty much everything he had.

" The expedition was so successful that Boston was very vain of the performance, and readily believed that her men had been very valiant and could take not only a little place like Port Royal, but a strong citadel like Quebec. There had already been talk of such an expedition, in connection with one by land from Albany against Montreal; and now, upon Phips's return, the Boston men set about collecting a fleet and army. They applied to England for aid, and, not waiting for her answer, they went on with their preparations. England refused, but Massachusetts thought herself quite equal to the task, and it was believed, besides, that enough booty would be brought back from Quebec to pay the expenses of the venture. A good many merchants advanced money on the strength of this expectation, and after vessels

and men had been pressed into the service, on the
9th of August, 1690, the fleet sailed from Nantasket
with twenty-two hundred men and provisions for four
months.   If it had been meant only to make a summer trip this might have answered, but they carried
only a small amount of ammunition, and they had no
pilot to take them up the St. Lawrence.   It was a
most foolhardy expedition, and yet it turns out that
if it had been under the lead of a true soldier, act-
ing with promptness, it might have been successful,
not by attacking Quebec in front, but by passing up
the river and climbing the heights behind the town,
where it was more exposed."

"Why, that is what Wolfe did," said Jeff.

"Yes; and Phips might have done the same.   Instead of that he delayed and delayed, and, finally,
when the French had had full opportunity to collect
troops and perfect their defenses, he appeared in the
bay below the frowning walls of the citadel, and sent
a messenger with a demand for surrender.   The governor of Canada was an old French officer, Count
Frontenac, who had the messenger blindfolded, so
that he might learn nothing of the interior of the
fortress, and then brought into the council chamber,
where he sat with his officers about him, all in splendid uniforms.   When the bandage was removed, and
the messenger looked about him, he must have been
very much astonished at the sight of these brilliant-
ly dressed soldiers, and quite prepared to tell Sir Wil-

liam Phips, when he went back, how contemptuously Frontenac treated the demand for surrender. Phips made plans of attack, and kept up a furious bombarding against the mighty rock. His guns made a great din, but did very little damage. His men were sick, the little expeditions which they made all failed, and at length he collected his little disabled fleet, and sailed away back to Boston, covered with disgrace. If he had only known it, and had held out a little longer, it is said that a famine within the town would have compelled Frontenac to surrender; but I do not believe he would have done this without making some effort to drive away the besiegers. The French were glad enough, however, to see Phips and his fleet sail away, and were only fearful lest they should fall in with and capture some vessels laden with supplies which were on their way from France; but no such good fortune attended the Boston men.

"The failure had one good effect upon Boston. It made the town begin to think that it was not very secure itself, and within the next few years a great deal of pains was taken to strengthen the defenses of the harbor, and a number of ships were moored in line of battle to annoy the enemy in case of attack. But their courage returned, and they determined to take Port Royal again, — a nest of hornets, as they called it. They sent out two expeditions, which resulted in nothing, but in 1710 they sent a strong fleet, which besieged the place, captured it, and changed its name to Annapolis, in honor of Queen Anne, who was then reigning over England.

"The greatest and most memorable expedition, however, was that of 1745 against Louisburg. Governor Shirley sat in the Province House, and was one of the ablest of the governors whom England had sent over. There was war between France and England, and New England men were fired with zeal to do some famous thing. There was more military wisdom now than when Phips sailed against Quebec, and the most careful preparations were made, for the fortifications of Louisburg were said to be very strong, and to have cost five millions of dollars. The expedition seemed almost as hopeless as Phips's, but it was planned and executed with greater care. For six weeks the siege went on. An English fleet assisted in the blockade, and at length, with scarcely any fighting, the garrison surrendered, and the immense fortress with all its stores came into the hands of the New England men. There are two mementos of the siege here. Louisburg Square was named in honor of it, and over the entrance to the college library, at Cambridge, you may see a cross which was brought away from the chapel at Louisburg. It was a great event, and I suppose nothing in the military way had so much to do with giving New England men confidence when the Revolutionary war opened as this triumphant expedition to Louisburg."

" But the English gave the fort back to the French, grandfather," said Jeff, who knew some history.

" Yes, three years later, when the treaty of peace was made between the English and French, Louisburg was restored, and some believe that it was part of the policy of England to keep the colonies here in check, for there had already begun to be signs of discontent, and the people were growing so strong that the English government was not sure what they might not attempt. Louisburg was taken again in the next French and English war, when Quebec also was taken, and Montreal, and all Canada passed into the hands of the English."

" Grandfather," said Benjy, when the old gentleman seemed to have finished, " you said there were five expeditions that sailed out of Boston harbor against the French in Canada. I have kept count, and there were only four, — the capture of Port Royal in 1690, Sir William Phips's expedition against Quebec the same year, the second capture of Port Royal, when the name was changed to Annapolis in 1710, and the taking of Louisburg in 1745."

" Did I say five ? The fifth is not one which I like to tell, and, besides, you know a good deal about it now. It was the expedition under Winslow in 1755, which reduced the forts in Acadia, and brought away the French Acadians and scattered them through the country. You know the story in Longfellow's ' Evangeline.' About two hundred families were brought to Massachusetts, but not many remained in Boston. They were sent inland to the country towns, for besides that they were chiefly farmers, the people had a fear lest they would slip away by water and get back to Acadia. There was an uneasy feeling in many minds, and I am sure that conscience was at work upbraiding the people for their cruelty. I should not like to have been Governor Shirley meeting Colonel Winslow when he came back to the Province House to report how he had obeyed orders, nor Colonel Winslow himself, who shows in his journal that he hated the business he had undertaken."

"Governor Shirley was not the last governor in the Province House, was he, grandfather?"

"No. The last was Governor Gage, and he gave it up to Sir William Howe, who occupied it during the siege of 1775–6. The Province House was a busy place then, for it was military headquarters. Opposite were some stables next to the Old South, and the Old South itself was used, you know, for a riding-school. So we can fancy the orderlies' horses fastened by the gate-posts in front of the house, guards pacing back and forth, and red-coated soldiers passing along the stone flagging and up the flight of steps."

"Well," said Benjy, "I wish the Province House was there yet; I'd like to see it; and then I should find it easier to imagine all these fine things."

"It has gone like the rule of England which it represented," said grandfather.

CHAPTER IX.

ONE evening, early in December, Jeff and Benjy were hunting for a game which they had mislaid, and looked in a secretary which stood in the library. In turning over the contents of a drawer they came upon a little leather case which they did not remember to have seen before, and opening it they found to their surprise an old silver medal. They spelled out the words on it.

"Why, grandfather!" they exclaimed, speaking to the old gentleman, who was reading his newspaper, "here is a Franklin medal, and it is dated 1814."

"To be sure: that is my medal. I had that when I left the Latin School."

"Why, did you have Franklin medals then? I knew the boys had them now, but I did n't know you had one."

"Why not, Jeff? Whom are the medals named from?"

"Franklin, I suppose."

"And who was Franklin?"

"Why, Benjamin — Benjamin Franklin."

10

" Yes, and I suppose you knew he was a Boston boy ? "

" Was he the first boy to have a medal ? "

" Oh no, he left in his will the money which is spent in buying the medals. Here, I will read you what he says in his will ; " and grand-father went to a book-case and took down a volume : " ' I was born in Boston, New England, and owe my first instructions in literature to the free gram-mar schools es-tablished there. I therefore give one hundred

pounds sterling to my executors, to be by them, the survivors or survivor of them, paid over to the man-agers or directors of the free schools in my native town of Boston, to be by them, or by those persons or person who shall have the superintendence or management of the said schools, put out to interest, and so continued at interest forever, which interest annually shall be laid out in silver medals, and given as honorary rewards annually by the directors of the said free schools belonging to the said town, in such manner as to the discretion of the selectmen of the said town shall seem meet.' "

" Who are the selectmen of Boston, grandfather ? "

" There are no selectmen now, Benjy, but when Franklin died Boston was a town and the government of the town was administered by ten citizens, who were chosen or selected out of the whole body in town-meeting each year, and so called selectmen. The towns all about us are governed so still. Now that Boston is a city, the people choose a Mayor and Board of Aldermen and Common Councilmen, and these take the place of selectmen, and the Franklin Fund remains and is held in trust by the city government."

" I thought Franklin lived in Philadelphia," said Jeff.

" He did live there much of his life, and died there, but he was a Boston boy. I 'm afraid you never stopped to read the inscriptions at the base of the statue in front of City Hall."

" Why, yes, I 've seen the statue plenty of times, and I have read the inscriptions, but I don't remember them."

" Then go there to-morrow, read them, look at the little bas-reliefs in bronze let in to the pedestal, and tell me about it when you come home, and see, too, if you can find where Franklin was born. But stay, I will tell you what to do. Walk down Milk Street, and look up at the Boston Post building, and see what you can find, and then go down to the corner of Hanover and Union streets. Walk down Hanover as far as Marshall Street, look carefully on both sides of the way, and then examine Marshall and Creek streets. To-morrow evening I shall want to hear your report, and then I'll tell you more about Franklin."

The boys left their grandfather to his paper, but the next day after school, they went on what they called a Franklin pilgrimage. They went from Bedford to Franklin Street, from a notion that they might find some reminder of Franklin there. They had fallen into the way of noticing the names of streets and wondering why they were so named, and as they passed through Arch Street, they looked in vain for any arch across it. They went through Hawley Street to Milk, and, crossing over, stood looking up at the Boston Post building.

" Well, I don't see anything," said Benjy, looking up as high as he could.

" Nor I," said Jeff, who was staring at the windows in the first story. They continued to look, and people who passed seeing two boys watching the building began to stop and look too, till a little crowd had gathered.

"Well, I never," said Jeff presently. "There it is, Benjy, in the second story : see, Birthplace of Franklin, and there 's his bust." The two boys had not noticed the gathering about them till now, when Jeff touched Benjy's sleeve and drew him quietly away. When they were at the head of the street, they looked back. There was the crowd still standing and staring. Nobody knew what his neighbor was looking at, and one after another dropped off, much mystified.

"What geese!" said Benjy, and walked off with his brother up School Street. They read the inscriptions and looked steadily at the bronze medallions.

"Now, Benjy," said Jeff, "we must remember just how these stand, for grandfather will be sure to ask us." It took them some little time to commit the statue to memory, but then they went on their way and stood for some time on the four corners of Union and Hanover streets, and strolled about among the neighboring streets, but look as hard as they might at all the corners, they could find nothing which had anything to do with Franklin. They made their report in the evening to their grandfather.

"We went first to Franklin Street," said Jeff.

"Yes, and we went through Arch Street," said Benjy," but I did not see any arch."

"You would have seen one a few years ago, Benjy. Franklin Street used to be one of the pleas-

antest streets in Boston to live in. It was laid out
a little after the death of Franklin, and named after
him.   All the lower part, that is from Federal Street

Franklin Street, just before the Fire.

up to about Hawley, was a low, muddy place.   A
great distillery stood near Devonshire Street, and the
land between Milk and Summer Streets was pasture

land. A Boston merchant first drained a part of the bog, and made a fish-pond there ; then afterwards a company of gentlemen made the ground more solid, and built a handsome block of dwelling-houses on the south side of the street above and below Arch Street ; where that is, they threw an arch across between two of the houses, and built chambers over the arch, so that one could drive beneath and come out in the fields near Summer Street. The Historical Society, and the Boston Library now in Boylston Place, used to have rooms over the arch. Then, on the opposite side of the street, were other houses with flights of stone steps and iron railings. I think the shape of the street is much the same now as then, a graceful curve, but in the middle of the broadest part was a grass-plot, inclosed with an iron fence, and in it stood an urn to the memory of Franklin. There were beautiful elm-trees in the street, and a great flag-staff stood in the grass plot. It is all changed now, and was changed, indeed, before the great fire. I was really sorry to see those generous brick houses taken down."

"So was I," said the boys' mother, who was in the room. "I was sorry, too, for I was born in a house at the corner of Franklin and Hawley Streets. We moved from it when I was four years old, and my very earliest recollection is of dragging a sled down its steps when we moved away."

"And did you find Franklin's birthplace ?" asked grandfather.

" Oh yes ; he was born where the Boston Post building stands."

" Yes, he was born there in a little wooden house ; I can just remember it, for it was burned down in 1810, — in this month, too, just seventy years ago. It stood end on to the street. The front was clap-boarded, and the upper stories projected over the lower, so that, I suppose, the rain and snow might be carried off from the house more surely. The door was on the west side looking up toward Washington Street. I believe it looked out on stables, but I am not sure. There were only two rooms on the ground-floor; the front one was about twenty feet square, and here the family ate their meals, and sat round the great fire-place; the kitchen was behind, and there were one or two chambers up-stairs. Here lived Josiah Franklin, the father of Benjamin. He came over from England in 1685, when people were beginning to be very discontented with King James, and he was one of those who sought New England that they might have greater freedom. He was a dyer in his own country, but there was not

Franklin's Birthplace.

much opportunity for this business in Boston, so he became a tallow-chandler and made candles, a very useful occupation then, when all plain people used them for light. There were seventeen children in the family."

"Seventeen children, grandfather!" exclaimed Jeff. "How in the world did they ever crowd into that little house?"

"That puzzles me, too, Jeff, but I think that perhaps the older children were apprentices and lived with their masters. At any rate, Josiah Franklin moved away from Milk Street when Benjamin was six years old, possibly because the house was too small, and went to live at the corner of Union and Hanover streets."

"Oh, that is where we went," said Benjy; "but there was no house there. I thought, perhaps, you sent us there to see where Franklin printed."

"No, that was elsewhere. The house where they lived is gone. Indeed, it could not be there, for the place where it stood was in Union Street; the street was widened, and the house thus had to be pulled down. I wanted you to go there, however, for another reason. Did you go by Dock Square?"

"Yes, sir."

"Well, then, you saw how little distance it was from what used to be the Town Dock. You know I told you that the water used to come up to North Street, and the wharves and ship-yards were off that street. When the Franklins moved, therefore, they were close by the water-side, and they were just as near, too, to the Mill Pond, for they had only to go a few steps on the other side, and they came to a bog where Haymarket Square is, and the bog was the muddy shore of the Mill Pond. Benjamin was sent to the Latin School at first, in hopes that he might go to college, but his parents were poor, and decided it could not be done, so they took him away and sent him to what was called a writing school. When he was ten years old his father took him from that school and set him to work at his own trade of making candles and soap. He had to cut the wick for the candles, fill the molds, wait upon customers at the shop, and run errands. He did not like the work at all, and wanted rather to be a sailor, for they were so near the wharves and the ships that all the busy life there seemed a great deal more attractive to the boy. He learned how to manage a boat, and to swim and dive, and he was very handy at everything which he undertook which required ingenuity and skill. I will read you what he tells about himself at this time," and grandfather took down Franklin's "Autobiography," and read : —

" ' There was a salt marsh that bounded part of the Mill Pond, on the edge of which, at high water, we used to stand to fish for minnows. By much trampling, we had made it a mere quagmire. My proposal was to build a wharf there fit for us to stand upon, and I showed my comrades a large heap of stones, which were intended for a new house near the marsh, and which would very well suit our purpose. Accordingly in the evening, when the workmen were gone, I assembled a number of my playfellows, and working with them diligently like so many emmets, sometimes two or three to a stone, we brought them all away, and built our little wharf. Inquiry was made after the removers; we were discovered and complained off; several of us were corrected by our fathers; and, though I pleaded the usefulness of the work, mine convinced me that nothing was useful which was not honest.'

" Franklin's father was a very sensible man, and when he found after two years that his boy was more and more dissatisfied with making soap and candles, he began to look about for something else for him to do. He used to take him on walks about town, and show him the different trades-people at work in their shops. You know in those days there were no machines working by steam, and no great factories. The only power besides a man's hand was horse-power, or water-power, or wind-power, and the carpenters did not buy their doors and windows made for them, but used their tools upon every part of the house. Even their clapboards and shingles were often roughly hewn, though they had saw-mills in the country which were run by water. So Franklin would see men busy at all kinds of work, — joiners, bricklayers, turners, braziers, shoemakers, wheelwrights, thatchers, ship-carpenters, cutlers, and printers, — and everywhere that he went he saw boys, some younger than himself, bound out or apprenticed to masters, so that they might learn the trade and work at it themselves. Benjamin Franklin liked all this; he was clever with tools himself, and was always contriving ingenious little machines at home. Finally his father decided that he would have him learn the cutler's trade; and as Benjamin's cousin, Samuel Franklin, who had learned the art in London, had just established himself in Boston, it was proposed that Benjamin should be apprenticed to him, but first he was sent to make a trial of it. Samuel Franklin, however, wanted a fee for teaching the boy, and although apprentices sometimes paid a fee, the father for some reason was displeased, and took Ben home again.

"All this time Benjamin Franklin showed a great liking for reading, and, while he had few books and few opportunities to borrow or buy, he made the most of what he had, and, seeing this taste, his father determined to have him taught the printer's trade. Mr. Josiah Franklin already had a son in the business, who had just come home from England, and he was very anxious to apprentice Benjamin to him, for he was afraid that the boy, with his hankering after the sea, would run away. So the papers were signed, and Benjamin Franklin was bound to his brother James for nine years. He was twelve years old, and from that time until he was twenty-one, his brother was to take care of him, feed him, clothe him, and teach him his trade, for that is what the master was bound to do for the apprentice. At first, of course, the boy would be an expense, and cost his master a good deal, but as he grew older the work which he did, and for which he received no wages, would begin to be valuable; and it was supposed that by the time a boy was twenty-one and had learned his trade, he would have paid back to his master all that had been expended on him, and more, too, so that it was customary, and included often in the papers, to pay an apprentice when he obtained his freedom, at twenty-one, a suit of clothes, which was called a freedom suit, and a hundred dollars. Perhaps it was because Benjamin was so promising a boy that his father required James to pay him wages during the last year of the apprenticeship. I wish it were more the custom to have apprentices now."

"Why, grandfather?"

"Because I think it is good for a boy to be bound fast to some honest occupation, to learn it thoroughly, and to look forward to the period when he shall be free; and because I think it is good for masters in a trade to be bound to take care of and to teach boys who are to learn. But these things are not so easily to be done now. Tell me, Jeff, what you saw on the pedestal of the Franklin statue facing School Street?"

"That is the front," said Jeff, "for Franklin is looking in that direction, and the inscription is, —

BENJAMIN FRANKLIN.

Born in Boston, 17 January, 1706.

Died in Philadelphia, 17 April, 1790."

" That is right.   And what is the bas-relief above ? "

" It is two boys printing."

" Yes," broke in Benjy ; " and we saw the very printing-press in the procession on the 17th."

" To be sure; and which of the two boys do you think is Franklin ? "

" I think it is the one by the press, with the copy in his hand."

" No," said Jeff, " I think it 's the other, — the one by the case correcting a page.   Is n't it, grand-father ? "

" My vote must be for Benjy.   I don't know why Mr. Greenough made Franklin reading copy, as we say, unless to show that when he was a printer's apprentice he was already able to do the higher work. Before his time was out with his brother he had become a diligent reader, and had even begun to write for a newspaper which his brother published.   To publish a newspaper in those days was a somewhat doubtful business; for though the old papers had not a great deal of reading in them, they were beginning to be the means which people used for making their complaints known, and those in Boston who did not think the government was treating the town fairly said so in the newspaper, and, as nobody signed his name, the government held the printer of the newspaper accountable. James Franklin was clapped into prison once because something offensive appeared in his paper, and he would not tell who wrote it. While he was confined Benjamin took charge of it, and was quite willing to print sharp words. When James was released it was on condition that he should no longer print his paper, and thus, to get round the difficulty, his name was taken off, and Benjamin's put on ; but for this it was necessary that his apprenticeship should cease. The two brothers did not agree with one another very well, and it was not long now before Benjamin left his brother and went to New York, and thence to Philadelphia, in search of work. That is the last of Benjamin Franklin as a Boston boy, for though he came back more than once to visit the town, he never returned to live here."

" Where did he fly his kite, grandfather ? "

" How did you know he had a kite ? "

" Why, on the opposite side of the pedestal is a bas-relief of a man and a boy flying a kite."

" And what is the inscription underneath ? "

" You tell, Jeff ; I can't remember."

" Eripuit cœlo fulmen sceptrumque tyrannis," said Jeff, promptly.

" And what 's that in English ? "

" ' Eripuit,' he snatched ; ' fulmen,' the thunderbolt " —

" Oh, give it straight off in good English, Jeff."

" Well," said the boy, stopping to collect his thoughts, " he snatched the bolt from heaven and the sceptre from tyrants."

" That is pretty well. Snatched sounds a little rude. Children snatch things, and I would call *cœlo* the sky and not heaven. However, you seem to have the idea, and what does it mean?"

" I am sure I don't know, unless he invented lightning rods."

" You know the story of Franklin's kite, don't you?"

" No, sir."

"Oh, I must tell you that then, though I supposed of course you knew it. What do boys learn at school? We all learned about Franklin's kite. By the way, which of the figures in the bas-relief do you think is Franklin, the man or the boy?"

" I think the man looks most like him."

" Quite right, and the boy looks a little like the man, for he is Franklin's son, William Franklin, who was about twenty-two years old at this time, and afterward became Governor of New Jersey, and was a royalist when his father was a patriot. But all this kite flying took place in 1752, before independence was much thought of. Franklin had long been busy studying electricity, which was then exciting students in Europe and America. He had written to his friends in Europe that he was very sure they would discover the electric fluid, which they were experimenting with by their machines, to be the same as the lightning in a thunder-storm; and he advised that a man should be placed in a box at the top of a high spire or tower, in connection with a pointed rod, to see if a thunder-cloud passing near would not give out its electricity to the iron rod. There was not a steeple in all Philadelphia where Franklin was living, so he could not make the trial himself, but like all ingenious experimenters he did not wait till the best means came. He set about a substitute for the best, and having no steeple, he happily thought of trying the experiment with a kite. He made his kite of a large silk handkerchief, which is a good conductor of electricity, and at the end of the perpendicular stick he attached a piece of sharp iron wire. He took his son William into his secret, and when a thunder-storm was coming up the two stole off with their kite to a piece of waste land on the outskirts of Philadelphia, where there was an old cow-shed. A hempen cord held the kite, but a silk thread was attached to it and held by Franklin, and between the cord and silk was a common door key; in the shed was a Leyden jar. William raised the kite, and I think he must have laughed at his father and himself, as he ran down the field before the coming storm, let the kite go, and saw it tossing and plunging, while his father payed out the cord. Then when the kite was well up, they both stood under the shed out of the way of the rain

11

and watched. The cloud passed over the kite, and nothing seemed to happen, but suddenly Franklin noticed that the fibres of the cord began to rise. It was what he had seen in William's hair when he had placed his boy on the electric stand " —

" Or rubbed a cat's back," suggested Jeff.

" To be sure. Then he touched his knuckle to the key, and a spark flew out. He charged the Leyden jar which he had brought with him, and proved unmistakably that he was right in supposing the electricity to be in the cloud. When the next ship came from Europe it brought the news that the experiment which he had proposed had been tried in a steeple and had proved successful. So Franklin at once became famous, and that is the reason why the words were used of him, ' Eripuit cœlo fulmen ; ' but why the other words, ' sceptrumque tyrannis ' ? "

" I suppose because he was so brave."

" Yes, Franklin was brave, not in the way of fighting but by his confidence in his countrymen, his hope and wise counsel. He was one of the best friends America could have in the great struggle for Independence, and it helped immensely that a man who had won such honor in France and England should be such an unhesitating and cheerful friend to American union. It had a great deal to do with the aid which France gave. But tell me what the third inscription is, the one which faces the sea. Come, Benjy, it 's your turn."

" Faces the sea ? that must be toward Washington Street."

" Certainly, certainly, but don't forget that there is something beyond Washington Street. Come, what is it ? "

" Why, the bas-relief is the signing of the Declaration, and the inscription is

DECLARATION OF INDEPENDENCE,
4 JULY 1776."

" That is right, and is n't it proper it should be on the side looking toward Europe ? I think so. Do you know why this appears under Franklin's statue?"

" Did he write the Declaration ? "

" He was one of a committee of five appointed to draw it up. Jefferson composed it chiefly, and there are a couple of stories told about Franklin in connection with it which I will read to you, rather than tell," and grandfather took down a book from the shelf and read as follows : —

" The delegates found a great many things to criticise and to alter in the document. ' I was sitting by Dr. Franklin,' says Jefferson, ' who perceived that I was writhing under these mutilations. " I have made it a rule," said he, " whenever in my power, to avoid becoming the draftsman of papers to be reviewed by a public body. I took my lesson from an incident which I will relate to you. When I was a journeyman printer, an apprenticed hatter, having served out his time, was about to open shop for himself. His first concern was to have a handsome signboard with a proper inscription. He composed it in these words: John Thompson, Hatter, makes and sells Hats for ready Money, — with a figure of a hat subjoined. But he thought he would submit it to his friends for their amendments. The first he showed it to thought the word *hatter* tautologous, because followed by the words *makes hats,* which showed he was a hatter. It was struck out. The next observed that the word *makes* might as well be omitted, because his customers would not care who made the hats; if good and to their mind they would buy, by whomsoever made. He struck it out. A third said he thought the words *for ready money* were useless, as it was not the custom of the place to sell on credit. Every one who purchased expected to pay. They were parted with, and the inscription now stood, *John Thompson sells hats.* ' *Sells* hats,' says his next friend; ' why, nobody will expect you to give them away. What, then, is the use of that word ? ' It was stricken out, and *hats* followed, the rather as there was one painted on the board. So his inscription was ultimately reduced to John Thompson, with the figure of a hat subjoined." '

"When the members were about to sign the document, Mr. Hancock is reported to have said, ' We must be unanimous; there must be no pulling different ways; we must all hang together.' ' Yes,' replied Franklin, 'we must indeed all hang together, or most assuredly we shall all hang separately.' "

" But now, Benjy, I must ask you one more question.   What is there on the side facing inland ? "

" It says

TREATY OF PEACE AND INDEPENDENCE.
3 SEPTEMBER 1783.

and there are four people, three at a table and one in the corner."

" Do you know who these people are and where they are ? "

" No, sir."

" They are the commissioners of England and America signing the treaty in Paris.   Franklin and Jay represent America, and Mr. Hartley England.   I think that must be a messenger who sits waiting in a chair.   So you see the sculptor has chosen four noticeable points in Franklin's life to engrave at the base of his statue.   He shows him a printer's apprentice, for his fame and fortune rest on the solid basis of industry and practical attention ; then he presents the philosopher experimenting, for Franklin's many discoveries were worked out by his own hands ; and finally he makes us see how Franklin's life was devoted to his country, how he was with the men who declared her independence, and with those who made the independence good."

" There is one part of Franklin," said the boys'

mother, who had been listening, " which does not appear on the statue, and that is his Poor Richard."

" No, we must look for it in his face, which is so kind and so shrewd."

" Who was Poor Richard ? "

" Franklin had a way of making little pithy, easily remembered sayings; and beginning them 'Poor Richard says,' so his maxims came to be called Poor Richard's sayings; and as these were printed in almanacs, which were read by people then as the newspaper is read now, everybody had them by heart. They were such sayings as 'God helps them that help themselves ;' 'Three removes are as bad as a fire ;' 'A penny saved is a penny earned.'   Some of the sayings I suppose were proverbs which Franklin had heard, and thought were needed by the people, and he printed them again, thus giving them new life.   For he was thought a very wise man by the common people, and his little sayings and stories were quoted very much as Æsop's Fables are."

" Were they not almost all meant to teach people to be economical, father?   I suppose in a new country like ours, he thought the first lesson we needed was to be taught prudence."

" Yes, Franklin was a great teacher of thrift and saving. He knew how much it helped a young man to lay by a little money every year and put it out at interest ; and he knew, too, how much a very little money would help a young man just setting up in

business. When he came to be an old man and to
make his will, he remembered the hard days he had
had in Boston, and how far a little money went which
was lent to him when he first set up for himself in
Philadelphia; he bethought himself of two thousand
pounds which the State of Pennsylvania owed him,
and determined to divide it between the city of Philadelphia and the town of Boston, for the help of just
such young apprentices as he had been. It was not
a great sum, however, and if it were given away it
would soon all be gone; so he made a curious provision in his will by which the principal not only was
not to be disturbed, but was to be added to every
year, and this was his plan. The thousand pounds
which he left to Boston was to be under the management of the selectmen of the town, aided by the ministers of the oldest Episcopalian, Congregational, and
Presbyterian churches. It was to be lent out at interest in small sums to young married mechanics, not
over twenty-five years of age, who had been apprentices in the town, and could bring two respectable
sureties for their bonds. As fast as the money came
back, the interest would be added to the principal,
which would thus be all the time growing. It would
be helping these young mechanics and gathering to
itself money all the time. The old gentleman was
very much pleased with this notion, and he began to
calculate how much the sum would amount to at the
end of a hundred years; and when he saw how large

it was, he was so pleased that he did another sum, and found what the whole would be at the end of a second hundred years. How much do you suppose he thought his thousand pounds would earn at the end of a hundred years, Jeff ? "

" At compound interest ? "

" Yes."

" And at what rate ? "

" He does not say, but you can do the sum if you want to. Franklin calculated that it would amount to one hundred and thirty-one thousand pounds at the end of a hundred years ; and so he made provision in his will that at the end of a hundred years, the managers of the fund in Boston were to lay out a hundred thousand pounds of it in public works, such as fortifications, bridges, aqueducts, public buildings, baths, pavements, 'or whatever,' he said, 'may make living in the town more convenient to its people, and render it more agreeable to strangers resorting thither for health or a temporary residence.' Then the remaining thirty-one thousand pounds he meant to have lent out again in the same fashion as the first thousand pounds had been, and for another hundred years; but at the end of that time the loan was to cease and all the money which had accumulated was to be given away. How much do you suppose he thought there would then be ? "

" A billion," said Jeff.

" A centillion," said Benjy.

" Oh, you won't be astonished if you guess such high figures. I shall have to set you at your slates. Franklin computed that at the end of the second hundred years his thirty-one thousand pounds would have grown to four million and sixty-one thousand pounds, and he directed that one million and sixty-one thousand pounds should be given outright to Boston, the other three millions to the State of Massachusetts, and that the trust should then cease."

" When will that be, grandfather ? "

" We have not come to the end of the first century yet. That will not be for ten years, and you will be young men then, and perhaps have something to say as to how it shall be used. But the sum does not look so large to us in our prosperity as it did to Franklin in the day of small things. The fund has been carefully managed, however, and will not fall far short of what Franklin imagined. But Boston is a very different place from what it was when Franklin fished for minnows in Haymarket Square, and served as an apprentice to his brother James. By the by, boys, when you were looking for Franklin's house at the corner of Hanover and Union streets, did you do as I told you, and look up and down Hanover Street, and in Creek and Marshall streets ? "

" Yes, sir, but we did n't find anything."

" Did n't find anything ! Why, where were your eyes ? I shall have to take you myself and point out with my stick what you ought to have seen. Be off with you to bed now, or I shall get my stick to-night." The boys scampered away, but grandfather was as good as his word, for the next afternoon he took them with him on a walk down Hanover Street. When he had come nearly to Blackstone Street, he stopped on the northern sidewalk, wheeled them about facing the buildings on the other side and bade them look sharp.

"I see it," said Jeff, first. "What is it? Is it a bas-relief?"

"It is a coat of arms cut in stone," said grandfather. "Noble families used to have coats of arms, somewhat as a nation has a flag, or a state has a seal, and besides great families, certain corporations and guilds had them. This is one, I believe, which belonged to the Painters' Guild. Can you make out the letters and the date?"

The boys made out the letters

C

T   K

but they were perplexed over the date.

"I can see a 7 and an 0," said Benjy.

"The other figures are not very distinct, but they are both 1. The date is 1701. And what is the motto at the bottom?" But neither of them could make it out. Just then a cart drove up to the door of the building where the stone was. A good-natured man jumped down from it, and grandfather crossed the street with the two boys.

"May we climb up to your seat?" he asked the man. "We want to get a closer look at that piece of carving." The man followed with his eye the direction of grandfather's stick.

"That! why I never saw that before. Yes, get up on the wagon if you like," and as they climbed upon the seat, the man himself stepped out into the street to get a look at the arms.

"Amor," began Jeff. "I can make that out. Amorque."

"Tut, tut, lad. Do they teach you in the Latin School that que follows the first word of the pair? Try again."

"Que — at, queat, is it, grandfather?"

"It looks like it."

"Obediencia," said Benjy, who had been giving his attention to the last word in the line.

"Amor queat obedientia, it is," said grandfather, "though the stone-cutter seems to have spelled the last word with a c." They got down from the cart.

"What do you make it to be?" asked the owner of the wagon.

"It is the coat of arms of the old Painters' Guild," said grandfather, "dated 1701, with the initials C T K, and the motto, Amor queat obedientia. What does that mean, Jeff?"

"I know love and obedience," said the boy, "but I don't know queat."

"Well," said the man, who had been listening, and

now turned to go into a shop, " if you know love and obedience, it 's not much matter about queat."

" What does it mean, grandfather ? " the boys asked as they walked along.

" I think I should translate it, ' Let love stand for obedience,' or, ' Take the will for the deed,' but I am not quite sure."

" And how came the arms here ? "

" I think it was brought over by a painter from England, who set up his shop here about 1700. See, here is Boston Stone." They had come to the corner of Marshall and Creek streets, and stood by the stone imbedded in the foundation wall, with its spherical stone atop. The boys read the letters and figures sunk deep in the stone.

" What is it ? " they asked.

" It is said to have been originally a portion of the stone paint-mill brought over by the painter. The upper stone was the grinder. Just how it came to be used as Boston Stone I do not know, and if there were not a London Stone we should be at a loss to understand what it meant at all; but in London there is a very ancient stone imbedded in the wall of a church and known as London Stone. It is surmised that it was the point from which distances were measured, like the golden mile-stone in Rome, and it was a fixed locality which people knew, and just as you see shops advertised now as opposite the Old South, so you would hear of shops by London Stone. It is my belief that Boston Stone was named so by some one who came over from London, and used to have a shop near London Stone, and so thought he would have his shop near Boston Stone, and had these letters and date cut. But I cannot tell you anything more about it, though I have been told that it was once used as a starting-point for surveyors."

CHAPTER X.

FANEUIL HALL AND SAM ADAMS.

As they came back from their walk that afternoon, they caught sight of Sam Adams upon his pedestal at the head of New Washington Street. The boys fell to wondering at the tea-table why the city had placed the statue just there.

"It is so that he can have an eye on Faneuil Hall," said Jeff.

"No," said Benjy. "I am pretty sure he was a ship-carpenter, and he was put down at the North End, where there were ship-yards."

"I think Jeff must be nearer right," said grandfather. "Sam Adams was not a ship-carpenter; his father, I believe, was a brewer, and lived on Purchase Street, but the Faneuil Hall which the statue of Sam Adams sees is not the one in which the real Sam Adams spoke. It is the third building which has been known as Faneuil Hall, but I should not at all wonder if Sam Adams was present when the first Faneuil Hall was opened. Peter Faneuil was a Frenchman by birth, the nephew of a Boston merchant, who came over from France when the Huguenots were persecuted, and made a large fortune here.

He left it to his nephew Peter, and Peter offered to
build for the town of Boston a market-house on land

Sam Adams.

near the old Town Dock, which had been filled in
and reclaimed from the sea. There was no market
in Boston at that time, though there had been three,

and for some reason people were very much divided
on the question whether there should be one or not.

The Faneuil Hall of the Revolution.

When Peter Faneuil's offer was made, a town-meeting was held to see what should be done.   The Town
House was not big enough to hold the crowd, and
they adjourned to the Brattle Street Meeting-House.
They fought over the gift, and finally accepted it
only by seven votes, three hundred and sixty voting
against it, and three hundred and sixty-seven for it.
The meeting was held in July, 1740, and Sam Adams
had just graduated at Harvard College, so I think
it is very likely indeed that he was present; for

his father was a prominent Boston man, and Sam himself had begun to take an interest in public matters. The hall was built, the lower part for a market, the upper part for a hall, and here the annual town-meetings were now held. At the very first meeting in Faneuil Hall I am sure Sam Adams must have been present, for Peter Faneuil had died, and John Lovell, who had been Sam Adams's master at your Latin School, gave a funeral address there before a thousand people. They hung portraits in the hall, as now, and one of the first to be placed there was that of King George the Second, who was king of England when the hall was built, and called by all good Boston people our Sovereign Lord and King, and His most Gracious Majesty. The town-meetings had been growing too large for the Town House, and the people found Faneuil Hall a very convenient place in which to meet. They had pretty stormy times in Boston then, and when Sam Adams had left college and was establishing himself in life, he had many opportunities for learning how the people felt and how they were talking. I am not sure but one reason why the town was so evenly divided over Peter Faneuil's gift was because there were two strong parties: the court party, which included the governor, all the officers of the crown, and a large proportion of the rich men; and opposed to the court party a large body of plainer people, the tradesmen and mechanics, with a few determined men who were their leaders.

12

At any rate there were some violent town-meetings about this time, or a little later, and uncommonly hard words were used. The people complained that Boston was not working for itself and its own prosperity, but for England ; that the English laws were made to draw away all the riches from Boston working people, and put the money into the hands of London merchants and a few men in Boston ; that taxes were growing heavier, and British naval officers were pressing Boston seamen into their service. You do not know what that means, children, but to our fathers it was a sore grievance. The British navy or the British army needed more men ; there were no volunteers, and the officers had power to seize upon men where they could find them, and press them into service. The law, indeed, had forbidden this impressment in the colonies, except in the case of deserters ; but British captains found a way to evade the law, and the Boston people complained in town-meeting in 1746 that they had lost lately as many as three thousand seamen from Boston, largely from this cause, for not only were a great many impressed, but still more had fled out of New England to escape impressment. There was in fact a riot in Boston the next year after this, which showed how strongly the town felt.

" Commodore Knowles, a British naval officer, had brought his fleet into Boston harbor and anchored in Nantasket Roads. The life of a sailor in the service was a pretty hard one then, and those especially who had been pressed without their own consent were very restless, so that there were a good many desertions from the ships. One day in November Knowles determined to fill up his ranks again, and sent his boats out to carry away from vessels that were just ready to sail such sailors as he wanted, and then swooped down on the wharves and carried off not only seamen, but ship-carpenters and boys. The town was all ablaze with excitement, and there was a rising among the mechanics in the north part, whose relatives had been seized. They caught up cutlases, sticks, stones, and tools, and began rushing through the streets, looking for some one to revenge themselves on. It was early in the morning, and happening to find one of Commodore Knowles's lieutenants, who had had however nothing to do with the affair, they laid hold of him and locked him up, and then started for the Province House, where it was said that several English officers were staying. Rumors of what was going on had got afloat, and some friends of Governor Shirley outran the mob and warned him of what was coming. Soon they surged into the court-yard and filled all the space there. The officers who were in the house drew their swords, and for a moment it looked as if there would be an attack, when a sheriff, with more zeal than wisdom, came along and ordered the mob to disperse. They turned upon him and dragged him along, laughing at his discomfiture and hooting at him. A mob is easily

turned, and all the people now left the Province
House to see what was to be done with the poor
sheriff. They dragged him to the front of the Town
Hall, where stood the stocks, and clapped him into
them, and were so entertained with this turning of
the tables that their fury was moderated a little, and
as they were getting hungry besides, the more part
went home to dinner, and in the afternoon there
were crowds and knots again of men who were consulting what should be done next. The General
Court was holding its sessions in the Town-House,
and meeting in the evening; when it was dusk and
work was done, the people began gathering before
the building, swarming from the wharves up into
King Street, in the great open space which you can
still see below the old State House. They called
upon the General Court to redress their wrongs, and
some of the noisier and more violent began to hurl
stones and brickbats against the building, and the
windows of the council chamber crashed in. Governor Shirley was a brave man and came out upon the
balcony above the crowd, and made a little speech,
telling them to be patient, that he was on their side,
and the General Court would see that justice was
done, but they must not be riotous. The crowd was
getting unruly and his words did little good, so he
took the advice of his friends and went back to his
house. Meanwhile the people demanded that all the
officers of the fleet should be seized and held until

the men who had been impressed were released, and
hearing that a barge had landed from the fleet, they
all rushed down to seize it. It was a mistake, though
they did not know it at the time, for it was a boat
belonging to a merchant vessel, but they seized it
and dragged it up in front of the Province House.
There they meant to make a bonfire of it, but reflecting that they might endanger their own houses and
shops, they dragged it off into the fields and burned
it there. The governor heard the cries and saw the
flames and determined to put the mob down ; so the
next morning he ordered drums to be beat to call out
the militia, but not a drum was heard. Then he saw
that he had lost control, and that the militia were
probably ready to help the people and not to put
down the riot. He withdrew to the Castle in the harbor, and now affairs began to look serious. The commodore declared that unless the officers who had been
arrested, were returned to him, he should draw up
his ships and open on the town. The town, on the
other hand, declared they would listen to nothing but
the return of the kidnapped men, and that they
would not give up the officers till these were sent
ashore. For three days this lasted. The General
Court passed a series of resolutions calling on the
people to sustain the government, but at the same
time saying that the wrongs should be redressed.
The people met in town-meeting and discussed the
affair, and as no blood had been shed, the talk was a

safety-valve, and most likely the best friends of the people, men like Sam Adams's father, gave good advice both to the people and to the governor, who was after all too shrewd a man to put himself in direct opposition to the town. The result was that the militia was called out again, and this time they came in great pomp and escorted the governor back to the Province House, but the price at which the governor purchased this peace was the restoration of all the kidnapped men. The British officers were released, and Captain Knowles sailed out of Boston Harbor with a pretty clear notion that the peppery little town had got the better of his majesty's government in the quarrel. But then he was in the wrong himself, and that was what made his side of the controversy weak."

"I wish I could go to a town-meeting," said Jeff.

"It would be worth your while to if you ever were in the country in the spring of the year. Then you would see how Boston used to govern itself. The notice of town-meeting at first used to be given from house to house, and every six months officers were chosen to rule the town, but after a few years, the time was changed to once a year. Then the notice for town-meeting came to be posted on the churches and in public places, and the day when it was to be held was so important that people did not mind their private business but flocked to the Town House, or, later, to Faneuil Hall. They came together in the

morning, and usually could not finish the business,
but when dinner time came adjourned to the afternoon, and sometimes had to adjourn over to another
day then ; and when Faneuil Hall could not hold all
the people on some exciting occasion, they would
adjourn town-meeting to the Old South or to Brattle Street Church. From the very beginning the
people had learned to rule themselves. The Charter
which they brought with them gave them the right
to choose their own rulers, and when they had once
begun to use this right in choosing the governor and
the members of the General Court, it was easy to
extend it to the election of town officers. Then, as
the towns increased in number, each was a compact
little community and had questions to settle which
they could only settle among themselves. They
needed some one to look after stray cattle, and they
chose a pound-keeper ; people littered up the shore
and wharves, so they needed a water-bailiff; they
had a market, and wanted a clerk ; and then they
needed men to have oversight of the different trades,
to weigh fish and hay and measure wood. They
were used to some of these offices in England, but
there such were appointed by the king; here they
chose them for themselves, and chose their own
sheriffs and constables. In this way everybody who
was a man grown had something to do with manag-
ing the town, and if things went wrong he could
make his complaint in town-meeting and get other

people who agreed with him to change the government. At first only those who were members of the church were allowed to vote, but afterwards all citizens could ; and even when the Charter was taken away, and governors were sent over from England, although the power was taken somewhat out of the hands of the people, they still had their right to vote, and had their town-meetings. At these meetings they would draw up instructions for their delegates to General Court. If they did not like what the governor was doing, and thought themselves oppressed by taxes or governed by unjust laws, they talked long and loud in their town-meeting, and drew up vigorous papers for their delegates. In this way the people were kept constantly vigilant and ready to defend their liberties, and they were so outspoken that the governor and his friends always had to be on their guard. At the first sign of anything that looked like injustice, the people were pretty sure to start up. The Knowles Riot showed what they might do, and it was not the last of the disturbances. Did you ever see the carving of the Liberty Tree in the face of a building at the corner of Washington and Essex streets, opposite the Boylston Market ? "

" Yes, sir."

" And what was the Liberty Tree ? " There was a silence, and the boys looked at each other.

" It was — I think it was a tree with a flag-staff through it," said Jeff finally.

" That's not a bad answer, but why was it called Liberty Tree? You don't know? Well, I will tell you. Where the corner of Washington and Essex streets now is was once an open green, and on the green stood some great elms. One of them was a very commanding one, and was said to have been planted in 1646. It had great spreading branches, and public meetings used to be held on the green, beneath it, which was known as Hanover Square. There had been a growing discontent with Great Britain, especially among the mechanics, the ship-builders, and

others whose business had been seriously obstructed by the laws made in England to govern the trade of the colonies. These laws had made a few men in Boston rich, but had helped to make a great many more poor, and yet these poor men had grown up with the right to help in the government of the town and with a pride in Boston. When it was learned that the British Parliament proposed to pass a stamp act, the people were loud in their indignation."

" Grandfather," broke in Jeff, " I never did understand what the stamp act was. I wish you would tell us."

"It was a bill which compelled everybody in the colonies, when he transacted any business which required a legal paper, to fix upon the paper a stamp which he must buy of the king's officers, or else it would not be legal. During our war for the Union, there was a law requiring every person who gave a receipt for goods which he sold to fix a stamp upon it, or else the receipt was good for nothing. We fix them still to bank checks, and to some legal papers and manufactured articles. We call them revenue stamps."

"Oh, I know revenue stamps," said Benjy. "I've got them in my stamp-book."

"And why are they called revenue stamps? What is the difference between them and postage stamps?"

"You put postage stamps on letters."

"Why?"

"They wouldn't go if you didn't."

"The stamps don't make the letters trot along, do they?"

"Not even if you lick 'em," said Jeff smartly.

"Tut, tut, Jeff. But tell me, don't you know what the stamp is for?"

"It must be to pay for the cost of carrying the letters."

"Exactly. We pay three cents to the United States for carrying our letter, and the stamp is a receipt for the money pasted on the letter. Now the revenue stamps are issued by the government to help pay the expenses of government. The law says to me, — You must bear your share of the expenses, and so whenever you draw a check at the bank, you must pay the government two cents, and the two cent revenue stamp which the government sells you shows that you have done it. The money which comes from the sale of these stamps is revenue to the government, its income with which it helps pay for the army and navy, and public buildings and courts of law, and pensions, and many other things which go to making it possible for us all to live at peace and bring up our families in this country. We are willing to pay taxes and buy stamps for this, because we choose the Congress which passes the laws imposing taxes and duties, and we agree each to pay these little sums for the general good. Now in 1765 we were colonies of Great Britain, and Great Britain said, — You must not buy certain goods from the West Indies, but your ships must carry them first to us in England, and we will sell them to you ; the goods will cost you a little more than if you brought them straight from the West Indies to Boston and New York, but that is of little consequence ; we want to make some money out of the business. The consequence was that captains and sailors and the merchants who owned the ships thought this very unjust, and began to smuggle goods into the country, to avoid paying duties on goods at the custom-house ; whereupon the English said that the officers

of the crown, if they suspected anybody of concealing
smuggled goods, could demand of the law court what
was called a writ of assistance, by which they could
enter houses and search for the goods. The people
were indignant at this, and were so roused that the
king's officers thought it prudent not to push matters. But the proposed stamp act created the greatest feeling. It was a direct tax for which they got
nothing in return, and it was a tax about which they
could say nothing. Hundreds of thousands of dollars
were to be taken from them, and it was said that the
money was to be used just to build a new palace for
the king in London. They said that if the king had
the right to tax them in this way when he wanted
money, what was to prevent him from laying a tax
upon their land itself, and of taking from them the
right of self-government which they had so long en-
joyed ?

"I have not forgotten Liberty Tree. One morning, it was the fourteenth of August, 1765, as people
came out of their houses near by, they discovered a
stuffed figure hanging from one of the branches ; its
dress, and some rude likeness perhaps to his face,
showed for whom it was intended — Andrew Oliver,
who had been lieutenant-governor a few years before,
and was now the officer who held the stamps, and
whose business it was to sell them. Near by hung
another figure, it was an immense boot, and out of it
was thrust a head with horns. Every one laughed

when they saw this last; they knew what it meant,
— a jest upon the Earl of Bute, an English nobleman
whom everybody believed to be the real originator of
the stamp act. There the images hung swinging in
the air. It was as much as to say, — Look at Oliver
and Lord Bute! We would hang them if we could.
It was the greatest indignity that could be offered,
but nobody knew how the effigies came upon the
tree. All day long people flocked from other parts
of the town, and came in across Roxbury Neck to see
the images and jeer at them. Lieutenant-governor
Hutchinson ordered the sheriff to take them down,
but the sheriff knew that if he attempted it there
would be a riot, and he refused. When night-fall
came, certain men appeared and began to take down
the figures. Nobody objected now, for these men
were known to belong to the company of citizens
called Sons of Liberty. They had with them a hand-
bier upon which they placed the effigies. They pretended these had hung till they were dead, and must
now be buried or burned. There marched off a
great procession of the Sons of Liberty, followed by
crowds of men, women, and children, that warm August evening. It was a still march. No one but the
Sons of Liberty knew what was to be done. Down
Washington Street, though it was not known then by
that name, they marched, tramping along to the
Town House. There were open arches below, the
council chamber being above, where the governor

and council were sitting. 'Liberty, Property, and no Stamps,' they shouted as they marched along, down King Street, and so along Kilby Street, to about where Water Street crosses it, and there they halted in front of the frame of a new building. The crowd set up a shout. It was a structure which Oliver was putting up, and everybody said it was to be the new stamp office. The Sons of Liberty began to tear down the timbers, and the crowd fell upon the frame with a will ; they hurled some of the sticks into the dock close by, and dragged the rest after them as they kept on their march to Fort Hill to Oliver's house. Here they made a great bonfire and burned the effigies. Some of the more unruly broke the windows of his house, tore up his fences to feed the fire, and tramped about his garden, and even got into the house, but before night was over the mob melted away. Oliver found it necessary to take refuge at the Castle in the harbor, and afterwards resigned his office."

"I wish I had one of the stamps," said Benjy, whose ambition was to fill his stamp book.

"I have seen pictures of the stamps, but I don't know that I ever saw one," said grandfather. "The stamp act was repealed, you know, but not before the people all over the country had shown by their resolution that it was impossible to enforce the law. They stopped business rather than pay the hated stamp tax. In Boston they made Oliver read his res-

ignation before a great multitude of people in Liberty
Hall, as they had begun to call the open space about
Liberty Tree.   In all the public discussion of the
time Sam Adams was a prominent figure.   He wrote
in the papers, he spoke in General Court, to which
he had been elected, and he addressed the people in
Faneuil Hall and under Liberty Tree.   There were
political clubs formed which gave opportunity to the
Bostonians to take counsel together and help form
public opinion.   For years there had been a caucus
club at the North End, made up chiefly of ship-build-
ing mechanics, and now this club took in some of the
prominent men like Sam Adams, whose father had
been a leading member, and James Otis, and Cush-
ing, Dr. Warren, and Dr. Cooper.

"When the news came of the repeal of the stamp
act, the town was full of excitement and joy.   What
is the nearest church to the Liberty Tree, Jeff?"

Jeff thought a moment, and then said: "The Hol-
lis Street Church — is n't it?"

"Yes, and it was also in 1766, the year of the repeal.   At one o'clock in the morning after the news
had come, the bell in the tower of that church began
ringing; then the bell in Christ Church answered,
and soon every bell in town was ringing.   Guns were
fired, and drums beat, and bands of music were playing loudly before two o'clock.   I don't believe there
was much sleep for anybody that morning.   The people hung flags from the steeples and tops of houses.

They kept up the excitement all day, and when night came houses were illuminated and fireworks were set off on the Common, more splendid than any one before had known. Rich merchants threw open their doors, and the town gave itself up to a general celebration. Every year afterward for several years the date of March 18, the day of the repeal, was celebrated by the people, as was also the 14th of August, the day of the outbreak against Oliver. The people would meet in Liberty Hall, under the tree, show the British flag from the flag-staff which ran up through the tree, sing songs, hear speeches, make long processions, and separate more determined than ever to stand up for their liberty. The leaders kept alive this spirit, for some of them were far-sighted, and began to see that their rulers in Massachusetts and the British Parliament were determined to show themselves masters. The Boston people, with the other towns, had secured the repeal of the stamp act, but they knew that when Parliament did this it also passed a resolution declaring that it had ' authority to bind the colonies and people of America in all cases whatsoever,' and that made it very certain that the struggle was to go on until one side or the other acknowledged itself beaten.

" And now came a sharper test in Boston. It was pretty clear to the governor that he had not much power. The selectmen of Boston seemed to have more authority, and Sam Adams was a great deal more influential man, and yet the governor held his office by authority from the king of England. When a schooner laden with molasses was seized by the custom-house officers for trying to evade the payment of duties, thirty Boston men went by night and took the schooner away from the keepers placed on board, and carried off the molasses. To be sure, the selectmen ordered it restored, but it was evident that the governor could not do it. He had been urging the British government to send a garrison to Boston, for he thought if he could have some regiments in town he could make people mind. Two or three little affairs like that of the schooner determined the government, and they sent troops. You see in England the king and his ministers troubled themselves very little about Boston. They knew that the colonies were growing rich, and they wanted to get all the money they could out of them; and when the governor wrote that the Boston people were troublesome and rebellious, they thought of nothing else than to make them mind, and what was better for this purpose than a good garrison of troops? There were indeed some men in Parliament — men like Conway and Barre, and Burke and Pitt — who were able to see that the Americans were Englishmen, to be regarded as having the rights of Englishmen; but to most of those in power they were a distant, subject people, to be ruled and made profitable to the merchants of London. In the fall of 1768 troops were sent to

13

Boston.   The people refused to furnish barracks for them.   They were indignant at what they felt to be an outrage, and since the town would not supply quarters, they were compelled to see soldiers encamped on the Common and quartered in Faneuil Hall and the Town House.   In the harbor commanding the town was a fleet of eight men-of-war, with more than a hundred and eighty guns.

" Nothing brings about a conflict so quickly as having your enemy always before you, and the presence of the troops inflamed the people terribly.   The governor meanwhile and officers of the crown felt that now they were more than a match for the Sons of Liberty, and began to threaten all sorts of terrible things.   Sam Adams and the other members of the political clubs were determined to have the troops removed, not only because they felt it to be an indignity, but because their presence was a constant menace, and the town was always in danger of breaking out into violence.   Exactly this did happen on the 5th of March, 1770.   Every once in a while there had been a scrimmage between the soldiers and towns-people, when clubs were used and heads broken. Each little encounter made bitterer feeling, and on this evening two young men were passing through an alley near what is now the corner of Cornhill and Washington Street, by some barracks which had finally been erected for the soldiers.   A sentinel was pacing there, and according to military custom challenged the young men, ' Who goes there?' They made no answer, or else a saucy one, and undertook to pass him. He put out his gun to stop them, and they tried to push by. There was a scuffle, and some of the soldiers in the barracks came out without weapons except such as they had caught up, a fire shovel, or a poker, or pair of tongs; they were too many for the young men, and drove them back through the alley. Thereupon there was a great crowding to the place. The people in the neighborhood were always on the *qui vive,* and rushed to the rescue. The officers called in the soldiers to avoid a fight, and the crowd which had come together suddenly, and were ready for any excitement, began roaming down the streets, and discovered another sentinel posted before the door of the Custom-House, which stood on State Street, where the building now is containing the Union and State Banks. A boy called out that he was the soldier who had knocked him down a day or two before, and the crowd, asking no better excuse, fell upon the sentinel, and began throwing snow-balls at him. He tried to enter the building, but the door was locked. He loaded his gun, and that made the crowd more furious; he began to call for help, and an officer near by sent a squad of six soldiers, and then dispatched a messenger for Captain Preston, the officer of the day, who was at an entertainment in Concert Hall, at the head of Hanover Street. The soldiers charged their guns,

fixed their bayonets, and stood in front of the Custom-House, holding back the crowd as well as they
could, which grew and grew, for the bells were now
ringing, and the whole town was in commotion.   It
was an unruly, angry mob of men, and when they
saw Captain Preston coming with a half dozen more
men they grew angrier still.   They began to taunt
the soldiers, and to dare them to fire.   ' Fire, if you
dare ! ' they cried ; ' Come on, you lobster backs ! '
for the British soldier, you know, wore a red coat.
Finally, somebody in the crowd struck a soldier with
a club.   This was too much for the soldier's patience.
Without asking for orders, he leveled his piece and
fired.   Instantly some of his comrades in the excitement, hearing the gun, let off their muskets at the
crowd, and the mob, as all mobs are likely to do,
turned and fled, for they had no fire-arms, and the
soldiers found half a dozen or more men wounded,
three already dead on the ground.

" The drums were beat now, and an entire regiment marched into the street.   The whole town began swarming into the place, but there was no longer
a mob.   Things had become serious, and the selectmen and principal townsmen were on hand.   The
governor appeared on the balcony of the Town
House, looking down the street, and promised that
there should be a full investigation.   Captain Preston
asked for a trial, and, giving himself up, was com-
mitted to jail.   The soldiers who had fired were also

placed in jail, and a company of citizens, to help keep order, patrolled the streets. The next day a great town-meeting was held in Faneuil Hall, and the people sent a committee to demand the withdrawal of the troops. Sam Adams was at the head of the committee, and they went before the governor, who tried to parley with them to gain time. He declared that he had no authority to send away the troops; that General Gage, in New York, was the only one who could do this, but that one of the regiments would be removed to the Castle in the harbor. This was in the morning; all day long people had been pouring into town over the Neck and by Charlestown Ferry. The meeting had adjourned till three o'clock to hear the report of the committee, and when the hour came there was not room in Faneuil Hall, and so the Old South was opened and the people rushed into that, but the street was full from the Town House to the Old South. At length the committee, headed by Adams, came out from the Council Chamber with the written answer of the governor. The crowd parted to make way for them, and when they entered the Old South the people kept silence to hear the report. The chairman of the meeting put the question, —

" ' Is the answer satisfactory? Those who are in favor of accepting it will say Aye.' The meeting-house was crammed with three thousand people. A single answer came, —

" ' Aye.'

"Then from the multitude burst a tremendous 'No!' A new committee was appointed, with Sam Adams still as chairman, to make a final demand, and while the people still stood and sat expectant, the committee went again to the Town Hall, where were the governor, — or rather lieutenant-governor, for

John Adams

Hutchinson held that office, Governor Bernard having gone to England, — and his council, and the British army and navy officers."

"Oh, I should like to have been there!" exclaimed Jeff.

"Should you? So should I, and I should like to see a picture of the scene. Years afterward John Adams was writing to a friend of this very event, and saying what a picture it would make. I will read you what he wrote," and grandfather took down from a shelf the tenth volume of John Adams's works, and read as follows : —

" ' Now for the picture. The theatre and the scenery are the same with those at the discussion of the Writs of Assistance. The same glorious portraits of King Charles the Second and King James the Second, to which might be added, and should be added, little miserable likenesses of Governor Winthrop, Governor Bradstreet, Governor Endicott, and Governor Belcher, hung up in obscure corners of the room. Lieutenant-governor Hutchinson, commander-in-chief in the absence of the governor, must be placed at the head of the council table. Lieutenant-colonel Dalrymple, commander-in-chief of his majesty's military forces, taking rank of all his majesty's councilors, must be seated by the side of the lieutenant-governor and commander-in-chief of the Province. Eight-and-twenty councilors must be painted, all seated at the council board. Let me see : what costume ? What was the fashion of that day in the month of March ? Large white wigs, English scarlet-cloth coats, some of them with gold-laced hats ; not on their heads, indeed, in so august a presence, but on the table before them, or under the table beneath them. Before these illustrious personages appeared Samuel Adams, a member of the House of Representatives, and their clerk, now at the head of the committee of the great assembly at the Old South Church.'

" It was late in the afternoon," continued grandfather, " and Adams knew that the matter must be
settled then and there.   He repeated what the town-
meeting had decided, that the answer was unsatisfac-
tory.   Hutchinson again said, ' I have no power to
remove them.'   But he had already agreed to send
one regiment, the most hated one, to the Castle.
Adams saw his advantage.   He stood before Hutchinson, stretched out his arm, which quivered with his
suppressed excitement, and said, ' If you have power
to remove *one* regiment, you have power to remove
both.   It is at your peril if you refuse.   The meeting
is composed of three thousand people.   They are become impatient.   A thousand men are already arrived from the neighborhood, and the whole country is in motion.   Night is approaching.   An imme-
diate answer is expected.   Both regiments or none.'
Ah, boys ! " said the old gentleman, who in his excitement had jumped from his chair and was pacing the
room, " would n't I like to have heard Adams say
that ! "

" And what did Hutchinson say, grandfather ? "

" He had to give in ! He had to give in ! He asked
the gentlemen around him.   They were wise enough
to know that thousands of men would have flocked
into Boston and compelled him to send the troops
away, and they told him so ; and Adams went back to
the Old South, and reported Colonel Dalrymple's
promise that he would begin to move the troops the

next day. It was a great thing, boys; it was a real victory, — the victory of resolute men without arms, but backed by justice, over two regiments of the king's army, and the affair was so famous that the regiments came to be called Sam Adams's regiments. They were his. He as the spokesman of Boston town really commanded them, and ordered them away. People called that affray on King Street the Boston Massacre ; it was a big name for what was a small affair, so far as numbers go, but it was a name which meant a great deal, and every year, until the war for independence made it less significant, the people of Boston came together on the 5th of March and held a great meeting, and listened to an oration by some distinguished man. It was their Fourth of July, for they knew that it marked the beginning of great events."

" What did they do with Captain Preston ? " asked Benjy.

" They gave him a fair trial, and two of the best lawyers in Boston — Josiah Quincy and John Adams — defended him. That was a fine thing, too. It showed that the Boston men were ready to submit to honest law, and were not merely a set of lawless rebels. Preston was acquitted, for it was proved that he did not give the order to fire. Of the soldiers, six were brought in not guilty, and two were convicted of manslaughter, but the extreme penalty was not visited on them. They were branded on the open hand, and then discharged."

" But there were troops in Boston when the war began, grandfather."

" Yes, they came back with Gage in 1774, for by that time England knew that she had estranged America, and that there were people here who were becoming every year more determined to resist her, if she continued to govern them according to her own notion, and for her own profit, without consulting them. It was when the English troops were in garrison that your Latin School boys found their coast spoiled."

" I know that story," said Jeff. " I have seen the picture, too, of the Boston boys before General Gage."

" Have a care, Jeff. Your history will have to be corrected. It was General Haldimand whose servant sprinkled ashes on the coast. Haldimand lived on School Street, between King's Chapel and Master Lovell's house, and the coast was down the hill along Beacon and School streets past the school-house."

" Well, they were Latin School boys," said Jeff.

" They were boys from your first class who went and complained."

" I 'm glad something happened as I heard it. Seems to me all the stories have to be told over again before they are told straight. And did General Haldimand really make his little speech about Boston boys ? "

" Let us believe that ! " said grandfather, laughing.

CHAPTER XI.

A SMALL TEA-PARTY.

JEFF'S birthday and his grandfather's chanced to be the same day, the twenty-fourth of December, and as it was the first day of vacation, grandfather proposed to give himself a holiday too.

"Come, boys," said he; "you've been pretty patient listeners to all my long stories about old Boston. Let us finish before Christmas. I'll tell you what we will do. We will take one final walk this morning. There are three places I want to show you, — Griffin's Wharf, the Old South Meeting-House, and Christ Church. Then if you want to ask your friend Jack Eliot to tea, we'll have a little tea-party, and I will wind up my stories this evening, and you won't have to listen longer to your old grandfather."

"Oh, but we only listen when we want to," said Benjy candidly. "I went to sleep the other evening."

"Did you, you young rascal! Then keep awake to-night, or I'll make you listen another year. Get your hats and coats, and be quick about it."

The walk which the three took that morning was not a very long one, and it took them over ground which they had traveled before, but grandfather's plan had been to show them Boston in the order of time, and he had come down in his stories to the Revolutionary period. To-day he led the boys to the old State House, which had been the central point of so many stories of Boston. He had a friend whose office was in the second story, looking down State Street, and he took the boys there first.

"See!" he said, pointing with his stick, "you are looking down King Street from the old Town House. We will pretend we are in the council chamber. The street only ran about as far as Merchant's Row down there, and beyond stretched Long Wharf, as far, I think, as you now see. Warehouses stretched on both sides for some distance, and then on the north side only, while a battery was planted at the end. It was the great approach to the town by water, and when British soldiers landed at Long Wharf they would look up the long narrow road before them, and see the Town House at the end. But our errand is to Griffin's Wharf, at the end of Pearl Street. It has been Liverpool Wharf as long as I can remember, but it was Griffin's Wharf in 1774."

"Oh, I know what Griffin's Wharf is famous for," interrupted Jeff. "That is where the tea was tipped over in Boston harbor; but, grandfather, I really wish you would tell us why the tea was spilled. I wish

VIEW AT THE HEAD OF STATE STREET.

you would tell us before we go down to the wharf. I never could quite understand why the Boston people objected to buying tea when it was sent over here."

" Because it was taxed," said Benjy promptly.

" But why should n't we have paid the tax ? " insisted Jeff. " We have to pay a tax on tea now — don't we ? "

" Yes. Every pound of tea that comes into Boston harbor is taxed by our government, and the merchant who has imported it, when he sells it to the grocer, adds to the price the amount of the tax which he has been obliged to pay the government."

" Then the grocer pays the tax and not the merchant," said Jeff.

" No, for he charges his customer a little more than the merchant has charged him, in order to make a little profit."

" Then the customer pays the tax."

" Yes, the last buyer pays what the tea cost the merchant to import, and a little more for the merchant's profit, and the tax which the government has laid, and the profit which the grocer makes ; but the customer has got something. He has the tea, and the money which he has paid for his pound of tea has paid for the labor which the Chinaman expended in raising it, and the captain in bringing it across the water, and the merchant who owned the ship, and the grocer who brought it to his door, and the government which made it possible for him to earn enough money every day to enable him to sit down at his tea-table with his family and take his cup of tea."

" Then he ought not to grumble if he is taxed for his tea," said Jeff.

" No, he has nothing to grumble about. He may complain that government is foolish and extravagant, and spends a great deal of money unnecessarily, and so makes him pay a little more tax on his tea, but some tax he expects to pay."

" Then why did people make such a fuss in 1775 ? "

" It was because the people in Boston said they were as much Englishmen as if they lived in England, and that it was unjust to lay a tax upon what they might choose to buy in London and order sent to them in Boston ; that when England made them pay a tax upon what she sold to them, she was treating them as if they were foreigners. England said to the colonies,—You shall not buy of any countries except England; and then she stationed men in the ports to collect taxes of the merchants upon all the goods which she sent over. The colonies denounced these taxes, and said they would do without the goods rather than pay them. In that way they gradually compelled England to withdraw the taxes, until at length there were few left. One of the most important was that on tea, and the friends of America in England tried hard to get this tax repealed. The colonies, to show their firmness, discontinued buying the tea, and as they had been great purchasers, there was soon a vast stock in England lying idle in the warehouses, for the tea kept coming from India and China. Now the English government was very anxious to have this tea sold, for it had a great deal to do with the East India Company, which imported the tea; it had lent the company a large sum of money, and wanted to get it back again. It could remove the tax, and all the people in America would eagerly buy the tea, but this it did not choose to do. England said, or rather Lord North, the prime minister, who was trying hard to please his royal master, said, — The tax is not much, but we won't admit that we have no right to lay it; we have taken it off from almost everything else, but we will keep it on the tea. Bostonians and other Americans said, — The tax is not much, but we won't admit, by paying it, that England has any right to tax us. Now Lord North imagined that if he could make the tea a great deal cheaper he could break down the opposition in America to the tax. The company that sold the tea was obliged to pay a tax of sixpence a pound before any was sent out of England, and then threepence a pound was collected besides in America. Accordingly Lord North removed the export tax of sixpence on all the tea they might send to America, which would of course make it much cheaper, but he kept on the threepence tax.

14

" As soon as this was known the people in America were angrier than ever. It was as much as telling them that they wanted tea more than they wanted their principles; that they had made all this fuss because the taxes had made their tea cost too much, and now they were more determined than ever that the tea should not be landed. Great meetings were held all over the country, and the people bound themselves by stronger promises not to take any tea at all as long as the hated tax was laid. By this time there had been established all over the country what were known as Committees of Correspondence; in every town there were leading men who took counsel together, and kept the men in other towns acquainted with what was going on. There were no daily newspapers telling everybody all the news at once, and there was no general congress to which the different colonies sent delegates to act for them; but these committees took the place of newspapers and congress as well as they could, and when any news from England affecting the colonies was heard in Boston, Sam Adams or Warren or Cooper, or some other member of the committee, would write at once to New York, or Hartford, or Philadelphia, and tell the committees there. In this way people were kept active all the time, and could advise each other, and they could all act in concert. So when the news came of the arrangement which Lord North had made with the East India Company, and that the ships had already started, letters flew back and forth, and in every great sea-port the leading men went to the governor and insisted that the ships should be sent back to England without being unloaded. In Boston Governor Hutchinson refused, and the people took the affair into their own hands. Meetings were held in Faneuil Hall and the Old South ; not only Boston men, but men from all the towns about, flocked in to discuss the matter. The committee, with Sam Adams at their head, had repeated interviews with the merchants to whom the tea had been sent, and letters passed back and forth, the merchants trying to gain time, and the citizens determined to press the matter to a conclusion. They had posted a guard over the tea-ships to make sure that not one ounce of

The Old South before the Fire.

tea was landed. This went on for nearly three weeks. Finally on Thursday, December 16, 1773, the last meeting was held when the final decision was to be reached. At ten o'clock in the morning people began to flock into the Old South to hear what Mr. Rotch, the owner of the Dartmouth, the chief tea-ship, would say. He came and said that the collector of the port had absolutely refused to give him papers by which the Dartmouth might be cleared and sent back to England. Everybody knew that two English ships of war were in the harbor commanding the channel, and that no ship could sail out without their consent. Mr. Rotch was bidden go to the governor, who was the collector's superior officer, and demand his papers. The governor meanwhile had taken pains to be out of the way, and had gone to his country residence in Milton. So the people sent Mr. Rotch to find him, and adjourned till three o'clock in the afternoon, when he was to come back and report.

"When three o'clock came the church was crammed with people. It was believed that seven thousand people were inside and out. There they waited for Rotch, and while they waited they listened to speeches from patriots. Sunset came and Mr. Rotch had not returned. It was dark and cold, and I think the people must have thought it very solemn as they waited and waited. At length the chairman put the question whether the tea should be allowed to be landed, and a tremendous No! came from the immense crowd. Six o'clock, and Rotch had not come. At a quarter past six Rotch came and felt his way to the stand. It was still and dark as he spoke. He had seen the governor, who refused to allow the ships to leave. As soon as he ceased, Sam Adams stood up and said, ' This meeting can do nothing more to save the country ! ' and instantly there was a tremendous shout and war-whoop outside the building. The people poured out of the doors, and in the dim light saw forty or fifty Indians apparently hurrying down Milk Street. They quickly guessed where they were going, and great crowds rushed to Griffin's Wharf. Come, Jeff ! Come, Benjy ! let 's go down there now," and the old gentleman, who had become stirred by his own story, clapped on his hat and led the way into the street. It was a bright morning and the streets were full of people — a very different Boston from that dark December twilight so long ago. They made their way down to Liverpool Wharf.

" It is changed a good deal, I suppose," said grandfather, " but I wanted you to stand near the place. My father brought me here once. He was a Latin School boy at the time of the tea-party, and was one of the crowd who followed the pretended Indians. All he could remember was seeing a great hubbub ; he could not get near enough to see the men at work, but he could hear the shouts and laughs as the boxes were ripped open and the tea tossed into the water."

" It must have been all planned beforehand," said Jeff.

" To be sure it was. There had been more than three weeks of discussion, and it was pretty plain how it would all end, but I don't believe there were many in the secret, and those who were disguised kept their own counsel very well. In those days there was a great deal of secret correspondence and counseling going on, for men knew that they could not tell what was to be done without it's getting to the ears of the governor and his friends."

"Was not any of the tea saved?" asked Benjy, as they walked up toward Washington Street, presently.

"Yes, one of the men came home with some tea in his shoes, and his wife wrote on a piece of parchment what the tea was, and put it with the tea into a bottle to keep. She knew pretty well that this evening's work would be remembered."

"Has the bottle been kept?"

"Yes, a Boston gentleman has it. There was one man too in the crowd who thought it would be a fine thing to carry off some of the tea, so he went on board with the rest, and slyly stuffed all he could into his coat pockets, and inside the lining. He was a Captain O'Connor, of Charlestown. One of the men who was at work destroying the tea saw him do this, and as the captain was leaving the ship, he sprang forward and caught him. O'Connor made a jump and left his coat tails behind him; Mr. Hewes cried out and let the people know what he had done, and as the captain tried to get away from the wharf, everybody in his neighborhood helped him on with a kick, and the next day Captain O'Connor's coat tails were nailed to the whipping-post in Charlestown."

" And what did the English do when they heard of it ?" asked Jeff.

" They shut up the harbor of Boston, Jeff. The Parliament enacted what is known as the Boston Port Bill, providing that after the 18th of June no person should load or unload any ship in the harbor. In this way they meant to punish the town, and no more effective punishment could have been chosen, for by this act Boston, which was the leading seaport in the country, lost all its trade at once. England treated the town as if it had been a foolish, naughty child, and said, — Pay for the tea which you have destroyed, and we will repeal the Port Bill. But Boston was made of different stuff. English men of war blockaded her harbor, and an English garrison came over with the new governor, Governor Gage ; but although thousands of people were thrown out of employment, nobody was found who was ready to take back what had been done, and all the towns about, and all the other colonies, agreed that they would stand by Boston."

By this time they had reached the Old South, and went in. The boys had often been there before to see the curiosities, but all the talk about the great public meetings held in it made them wish to see the building once more. They wandered about among the curiosities, and looked at the portraits, and wished in vain that the old pulpit was back, beneath the sounding-board.

"It would be easier then to imagine Warren making his famous oration here," said grandfather.

"Was he one of the speakers at the tea-meeting?" asked Jeff.

"Most likely he was, but I was remembering the oration which he made a few weeks before the Battle of Lexington, at the anniversary of the Boston Massacre. You know I told you that for several years the people met on the 5th of March, to hear an oration and keep alive their indignation against the British. This year, 1775, the 5th of March came on Sunday, and they meant to have their celebration on Monday. The town was full now of British soldiers, and more were expected the next month. Fortifications had been thrown up in different directions, and the Boston people saw with bitterness that they were treated as a conquered town. All the while, however, the leaders of the people were growing more active and more secret in their preparations for resistance. Letters were flying back and forth, and frequent meetings were held. The governor had done and was doing all he could to keep down the people. An act had been passed prohibiting the calling of town-meetings, but the Boston people had adroitly evaded the act by adjourning their meetings from time to time, so that they called no new meeting, but kept the old one alive, much to the perplexity of the governor, who did not dare go a step farther and break up an existing meeting. When the time drew

near for the celebration of the 5th of March, it was
given out that any man making an oration at that
time, and especially any one making any reflection
upon the royal family, was liable to arrest and capital punishment. I think that Governor Gage, who
was a weak man, really tried to frighten the leaders
into silence. Of course his threat had just the opposite effect; it only made the leaders more resolute,
and led to the selection of one of their most prominent and bravest men, Dr. Joseph Warren.

" When Monday morning came, the people met in
Faneuil Hall, but soon for want of room had to adjourn to this building, where they had voted to have
the oration. They sent a committee to wait on Dr.
Warren, who lived in Hanover Street, where the
American House now is, and asked him to give the
oration at half after eleven o'clock that morning.
The pulpit here was draped in black, and the leaders
of the people were assembled behind it, while a great
crowd filled the house, and some forty British soldiers in uniform were directly in front and occupying
even the pulpit stairs. They had threatened to break
up the meeting, and Adams had politely given them
the most conspicuous seats in the house. We can
imagine how angry the people were. Before them
was the hated red coat which had occasioned the very
bloodshed five years before, now to be commemo-
rated, and the presence of a great body of troops in
town was a reminder of the loss of their liberties.

It would not take much to cause a riot in the meet-ing-house, for people when they are angry do not

Joseph Warren.

usually stop to count the cost.   The soldiers on their side were angry also, for they had been provoked

and insulted by the people, and some of the hot-
headed ones were quite ready to break out.   The
church was packed with people waiting for the orator.   At last he came, driving in a chaise to the
door, and went into an apothecary shop on the opposite side of the street.   There he put on the gown
which orators wore and came out.   But it was impossible to squeeze through the crowd, and besides it
was not well to create any disturbance by trying to
get in, so some of his friends got a ladder and placed
it against the side of the building, just under a window which was back of the pulpit.   The window was
open, Warren climbed the ladder, gathered his robe
about him, and stepped into the pulpit, where he
stood before the people.   He made his speech, which
was spirited and courageous.   He denied that Boston people were rebellious ; they demanded only
their rights as British freemen.   The soldiers below
coughed and hemmed and tried to interrupt him by
all sorts of noises, but he kept on.   While he was
speaking and exhorting the people to stand fast by
their colors, a young officer who was upon the pulpit stairs took a handful of bullets out of his pocket,
and held them up for the orator and anybody else to
see.   It was as much as to say, — Talk as much as
you please; we have these, and they will say the
last word.   Warren saw him ; he merely dropped his
handkerchief upon the bullets and covered them with
it, and went on with his oration.   It was as much as

to say, — Put your bullets out of sight, my fine fellow; they don't frighten me. Ah! it was not many weeks after that when Warren fell at Bunker Hill."

"Perhaps one of those very bullets struck him," said Benjy.

"Perhaps so. But come, we have one other place to see. We'll go to Christ Church. It is a bright morning, and not very cold. We'll see what we can see there."

Christ Church.

Although the boys had been born in Boston, and always lived there, they had never yet been inside of Christ Church. They had passed it, indeed, when they went with their grandfather to hunt for what they still called the Smugglers' Cave, and they had read the inscription on the tablet in the tower. To-day there were people busy dressing the church for Christmas, so they found entrance easy. The church has not a large congregation; many of its members have died or moved away, but every Sunday a good many visitors go there because of the fame of the building. They are shown the curiosities, — the old Prayer Book and Bible given by King George the Second; the old organ, and the four wooden figures upon the railing in front of the choir seats.

"Those were for holding candles," said grandfather, " and are said to have been taken from a French ship by one of Captain Gruchy's privateers. They were intended for a cathedral in Montreal, I believe, but found their way to this church instead."

They saw the bust of Washington against the wall, the earliest monument to him, it is said, which was raised in the country. But after all, the chief interest to the boys' minds was in the connection of Paul Revere with the church. They knew the famous story of Paul Revere's ride, and were eager to climb the steps of the tower to see for themselves the place where the lanterns were hung, so grandfather found the sexton, and asked him to lead them up.

"It is pretty cold up there," said the sexton, " for it's all open you know, but if you want to try it I 'll take you. Many a time on a hot summer day, when it was so stifling below I could hardly breathe, I 've climbed up into the belfry and found it as cool as on top of a mountain. But come along," and he led the way.

"Now we're going up the very staircase," said Benjy, as they tramped along.

"Perhaps you are," said the sexton, "but the steeple is n't the same. It was blown down in a great gale in 1804, and they put up this one, which is sixteen feet shorter, but I believe it looks like the old one."

"Oh, dear!" said Jeff; "seems to me nothing is the same. Faneuil Hall and the Old South and the Old State House are all different. I wish there were something that looked just as it did two hundred years ago."

"Why, look here," said the sexton, who was quite philosophical. "'T is n't in reason to complain. Houses change and cities change, just as people do. You can't wear this jacket you've got on twenty years from now, but you'll be the same person."

"Well said," said grandfather; "but I know how the boy feels. I like old Boston, but, after all, we don't want it to be a great museum. Even this church I'd rather keep for the sake of the people who can worship in it on Sunday, and learn to love God and honor their country. Then if a chance ever came again, they'd be ready to hang lanterns out, or show an electric light, if that was any better."

They found it pretty breezy and cool in the open tower, and buttoned their coats tightly about them, and pulled their hats down. They looked off across the water to Charlestown. How narrow the river looked; how near the other side!

" I'm sure any one over there could see the lan-terns," said Benjy.

" But who do you think hung the lanterns ? " asked grandfather of the sexton ; " Robert Newman or Cap-tain Pulling ? "

" Well, now, I tell you what I think. You see Newman was a young man, a young Englishman, and Captain Pulling was an old man. He was a patriot and a friend of Paul Revere's, and a vestryman. It would have been a pretty difficult thing for him to have climbed up here in the night-time, and hung those lanterns. Well, supposing he sent Newman up with them, and told him what to do ? Don't you see then any one could say that either of them hung the lanterns out ? It's like this. You build a house ; but say I'm a carpenter, and I do the building. You can tell people you built the house, and I can say I built it, and we'd both be true."

Grandfather shook his head.

" That does n't quite convince me," said he. " Pull-ing was not so very old. He was less than forty years of age. He was a patriot, too, for he was one of those who helped make Boston harbor into a tea-pot, and I don't believe he would have given over such a dangerous thing as hanging out the signals to a young fellow who might not have been in the secret. He would n't have saved his own head, and he might have endangered Newman's. No, no, de-pend upon it, Pulling, who had to hide and get out of the town, was the man who did it, and Newman, who stayed here and was let alone, had nothing to do with it, except to give up the key to Pulling."

Hanging the Lanterns.

"It is n't so easy to get rid of an old story," said the sexton. "There are hundreds of people who have heard that Newman was the man to one who knows the name of Pulling."

" That is true," said grandfather, " and we must n't do any injustice to the sexton. Many an obscure man has done an heroic deed and somebody else has had the credit of it. So here 's to the health of Pulling and Newman ! "

They stopped to look at the bells which hung in the tower, eight of them, all cast by Abel Rudhall, of Gloucester, England, in 1744. Separately they told the story that they were the first chimes cast for the British empire in North America ; that Governor Shirley was governor then, and that the church was twenty-one years old when the bells were hung.

" That was the height of British power in New England," said grandfather. " When the bells first rang, Sam Adams was just out of college, and Boston was still a loyal British town, and the colony had a governor who was ambitious to show that New England could make war and have riches and a prosperous trade as well as the old country. But there was something better for New England and Boston than to be just an echo of Great Britain."

" What a fine place this must have been from which to see the battle of Bunker Hill," said Benjy.

" So General Gage thought, Benjy, if tradition is true, for the story goes that he climbed these stairs and watched the progress of the battle here."

" Is n't this the steeple that Dr. Holmes means in his story, — you know, the poem that I 've read."

" You mean his ' Grandmother's Story,' Jeff.　No, it was hardly this steeple, if General Gage was here. It may have been the steeple of what was called the New Brick, which was built in Hanover Street a year or two earlier than Christ Church.　I fancy all the steeples and high places, especially at this end of the town, were occupied by people at that time watching the battle.　And when the people were shut up in town during the siege of Boston, some of the bolder used the spires as high points from which to make signals to their friends in camp."

" I don't see," said Jeff, as they walked home, " how there could have been a siege of Boston.　Why, if Washington and his army had fired they might have hit some of their friends here, and have hurt the houses too, and if General Howe had wanted to march out of town, could n't he have gone ?　He could take his ships and sail away at any rate."

" Yes, that is just what he did.　Washington could not have shut up the British in Boston so that they could not possibly get away, for he had no fleet, but he could get near enough to the town to fire shot and shell in and do a great deal of damage, and that is what he was ready to do when he built the earth works on Dorchester Heights.　Some day you must go there and see how the place commands the town. You can't have war without doing damage and bringing a great deal of misery.　If Washington had peppered Boston in order to drive the British out, or make them surrender, some of the men who fired the guns would have been pretty sure that they were injuring their own property. When the patriots went from Boston and gathered in the camps outside, they were willing to show General Howe that they did not care for Boston unless they could live there as free men."

" Did they all leave the town ? "

" No, most of the leaders left, but there were some merchants who stayed to keep guard over their property, and there were a good many poor people who could not get away."

" But why did n't General Howe march out, grandfather, before General Washington got his powder ? He had a good army, and he might have beaten the Americans."

" What good would it have done him to march out ? he would only have had to march back again. He would have been in the country amongst enemies, and if the American army had broken up and scattered, it could have come together again. Besides, Jeff, you must remember that it had not yet been decided that there really was war. To the British soldier there was a company of rebels who had fired on his majesty's troops ; there was no government sending out an army to meet the British army ; and General Howe was not sure but it would all blow over and the Americans lay down their arms. He thought it was a quarrel about taxes, and that

Parliament might possibly settle it without a fight. His business was to hold Boston and blockade its harbor. I think he must have been very much annoyed at finding himself shut up in Boston."

" They could n't go into the country," said Benjy.

" They did not want to go. The soldiers were in garrison, and it was of very little consequence to most of them where they were. The officers found the Tory families very polite to them, and they tried to enjoy themselves here, but it was somewhat dull, and then nothing came into town except by water, and they found themselves, and the people, too, forced to live sometimes on rather poor provisions. I think the state dinners given at the Province House must have been rather dismal affairs. When 1 was a young man I went once to see a couple of old ladies who were daughters of a famous Boston minister. Their father was a Tory, and they were Tories too. They had been young girls during the Revolution, and they had lived through a second war with Great Britain, but they were very proud of calling themselves English still. They asked me politely to sit down in a particular chair, and then told me triumphantly that I was under the English crown, for a picture of the man they called their sovereign hung just above it. They talked of how they used to walk in the Common leaning on Lord Percy's arm, and how he had his band serenade them. It was very amusing to the people about them; there they lived with all their old things, and made believe as hard as they could that there had been no Revolution, and that Boston was still an English town. One of them wrote to King William when he came to the throne, for they had met him when he was a young man, and she wished to assure him that they were still faithful and loyal British subjects."

The walk had brought them home again, and it was nearly dinner time. After dinner Jeff and Benjy went off to find their friend Jack Eliot and invite him to tea. Jack lived in Roxbury, but was staying for a few days at his uncle's in Boston, and always found it easy to take tea at Mr. Callender's. His uncle lived at the South End, and he was very proud of the fact that where the house stood had once been water. "Anybody," he said, "could build a city on dry land, but it takes a good deal to fill up a bay and build on that."

CHAPTER XII.

BOSTON CITY.

THE boys were used to what they called Jack Eliot's brag, and they were so constantly reminded by their grandfather of old Boston that they felt themselves called upon to take up the cudgels for their ancestors, and to maintain that the Boston of to-day was a very tame and uninteresting city compared with the town of Sam Adams and Benjamin Franklin.

"Grandfather," Jeff said after tea, "I don't think Jack cares much for old Boston. He is always talking of what Boston is going to do or to be."

"Well," said Jack, "I believe that if Winthrop or Sam Adams or Franklin could see our Boston now they would think a good deal more of it than of the dingy little town they knew."

"Dingy little town!" exclaimed Benjy. "Why it must have been a great deal sunnier and cleaner than it is now. You could go right down a lane to the water. It must have been something like what Hull is now, or Hingham."

"Jack," said grandfather, "what do you think is the most famous thing in Boston to-day, or what would you take a friend to see first ? Stop, you may each write on a slip of paper, and, Sarah, do you do the same, and we 'll see what comes out.''

" Well, grandfather, you must, too,'' said Benjy.

" So I will. Now, think well.'' There was considerable silence in the room, after the paper and pencils had been brought out, and the boys looked at each other and at the ceiling. At length Jack said he was ready, and presently the others, looking a little doubtful, laid aside their pencils.

" Come, Jack,'' said grandfather, " let us hear what yours is.''

" Commonwealth Avenue,'' said Jack, promptly.

Commonwealth Avenue

" I 'd start from the Public Garden and walk down the whole length, and then show them how much farther it was going, and what splendid buildings it was going to have on it.''

"Well, that would be a fine thing to show."

"And I'd tell them," went on Jack, "that the land was all made land, every bit of it, and that when it was finished it would be the broadest and finest avenue in America."

"There's a little bit of brag in that last, Jack; but if you were to say the Back Bay generally, I think you would name the finest show that Boston city has to offer."

"I wrote Back Bay," said the boys' mother.

"But I thought it wouldn't count to take such a big thing," said Jack. "It's like sweeping your hand round half a circle, and saying, 'So much of Boston.'"

"It was rather general," she laughed; "but I was thinking of that great group of buildings, finished and unfinished, which is to make a few acres of land there renowned. One of these days a person standing in Trinity Square will be able to see Trinity Church, the Museum of Fine Arts, the Museum of Natural History, the Institute of Technology, the Public Library, the Art Club, the Normal Art School, and the Medical College."

"He can't see the Public Library from there," objected Benjy.

"Not now, but he will when the new one is built."

"It's a fine thing," said grandfather, "a very fine thing, and when Boston has all those great shows, and thousands of men and women and young men

THE MUSEUM OF FINE ARTS.

and young women are studying art and literature and science and medicine, I hope they'll not forget the small beginnings of the town. But come, Benjy, what did you set down ?"

" I put down Bunker Hill Monument."

" To be sure, to be sure," said grandfather ; " I had quite forgotten that Bunker Hill was in Boston now. It 's a good thing to show, Benjy ; it 's a granite spike driven into the ground to show where Boston men went out to meet the enemy, and did not wait for the enemy to come to them. It 's a granite forefinger pointing up to the sky to remind us that the men who fought there prayed to God first, because they wanted to be on His side. Now, Jeff, what 's your word ?"

" I put down two," said Jeff; " Faneuil Hall and the State House."

" That was n't fair," said Jack.

" Well, I could n't tell which."

" I don't wonder, Jeff," said grandfather; " for the Cradle of Liberty was on the place where the townspeople met and made the laws which governed the town, and there they met when they looked each other in the face and said they would not give up their liberty. The State House is a larger Faneuil Hall, and it holds the public life of the people. Boston town has always been the capital of the colony, or the province, or the commonwealth, and it would be a small life only that the town led if it forgot that here the State had its head and did its thinking; that under the great gilt dome the governor and senate and representatives of all the towns met and counseled for the good of the whole State. It would be a selfish city that forgot how the railway trains were rushing in all day long from the country bringing people and goods; how the country was feeding the city, and giving its best blood all the while toward making it greater and richer and stronger. I was pretty near you in my choice myself, Jeff."

"Were you, grandfather? What did you put down? Was it where the Hancock House stood? Was it the Common?"

"No, I'll tell you what it was. If I had a young fellow come to see me, who wanted to see the finest thing in Boston, I think I'd just take him up to the cupola of the State House, and show him Boston itself."

"Well, to be sure."

"Yes," said grandfather, who had got up from his chair, and was pacing back and forth in his excitement, "I'd point him to the reservoir below, and show him that there, close at hand, stood the great Beacon, with its tar-barrel hung at the top to give warning to the people in the country if there was danger in Boston; I'd tell him that the tar barrels burned fiercely on the 18th of April, 1689, when it was known that the Prince of Orange had landed in England, and all the people flocked to Boston to drive the hated Andros out; and that again a fresh tar-barrel was hung up there when news came, in

1768, of a British army sent to Boston. I'd show him the roof of Faneuil Hall and the spire of the Old South and Christ Church steeple and Bunker Hill Monument. He should look out to sea and see the steamers coming and going; and inland, and watch the railway trains; and down on the wharves, and up at the grain elevators. He should think how Boston was

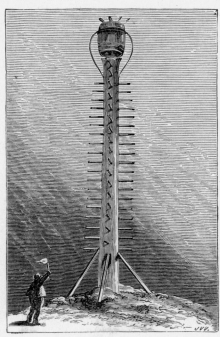

The Beacon.

stretching her iron arms across the great West and to Mexico, and sending her ships around the world. Then I'd have him look down on the green Common, and see the boys and girls playing; and I'd try to show him the house where blind Prescott wrote his histories, and the places where Webster lived, and Everett, and Sumner. He should see the Blind Asy-

lum over in South Boston, and the hospitals, the
school buildings, and the library and the churches,
and I 'd tell him, I 'd tell him " —

" What would you tell him, grandfather ? " Grandfather did not speak for a moment; then he went
on, —

" I 'd tell him that all these things were done by
men and women ; that a great and noble city could
only be where there were great and noble men and
women, who feared God and loved men, and that
when there were such men and women the city
would live and grow and be a blessing. Jeff," he
asked suddenly, " what is the motto of the city ? "

" I don't know."

" I do," said Jack promptly ; " it 's on one of the
gates to the Common, *Sicut patribus sit deus nobis.*"

" And what does it mean, Jack ? "

" May God be with us as he was with our fathers."

" That 's it, my lad.   And who were our fathers,
Jeff ? "

        " ' Pater, avus, proavus, abavus, atavus, tritavus,' "
said Jeff with great promptness.

" You 've learned your lesson well, Jeff. Aye, God
was with them all. That was what made Boston town.
Now you may have your games, but not till I 've read
you a grand poem on our dear Boston by the poet
Emerson, who once lived here and always loved the
town."   Grandfather took down a book from the

shelf, adjusted his great magnifying glass, which he
used when he read, and so half read, half chanted the

Trinity Church.

poem, while the boys and their mother and Jack Eliot
listened.   Long may they remember —

BOSTON.

Sicut patribus sit deus nobis.

The rocky nook with hill-tops three
　　Looked eastward from the farms,
And twice each day the flowing sea
　　Took Boston in its arms;
　　　　The men of yore were stout and poor,
　　　　And sailed for bread to every shore.

And where they went on trade intent
　　They did what freemen can,
Their dauntless ways did all men praise,
　　The merchant was a man.
　　　　The world was made for honest trade, —
　　　　To plant and eat be none afraid.

The waves that rocked them on the deep
　　To them their secret told,
Said the winds that sung the lads to sleep,
　　" Like us be free and bold! "
　　　　The honest waves refuse to slaves
　　　　The empire of the ocean caves.

Old Europe groans with palaces,
　　Has lords enough and more;
We plant and build by foaming seas
　　A city of the poor;
　　　　For day by day could Boston Bay
　　　　Their honest labor overpay.

The noble craftsman we promote,
　　Disown the knave and fool;

Each honest man shall have his vote,
  Each child shall have his school.
    For what avail the plow or sail,
    Or land or life, if freedom fail?

We grant no dukedoms to the few,
  We hold like rights, and shall, —
Equal on Sunday in the pew,
  On Monday in the mall.

The wild rose and the barberry thorn
  Hung out their summer pride
Where now on heated pavements worn
  The feet of millions stride.

Fair rose the planted hills behind
  The good town on the bay;
And where the western hills declined
  The prairie stretched away.

What rival towers majestic soar
  Along the stormy coast, —
Penn's town, New York, and Baltimore,
  If Boston knew the most!

They laughed to know the world so wide;
  The mountains said, " Good day!
We greet you well, you Saxon men,
  Up with your towns and stay! "
    The world was made for honest trade, —
    To plant and eat be none afraid.

" For you," they said, "no barriers be,
  For you no sluggard rest;
Each street leads downward to the sea,
  Or landward to the west."

Oh, happy town beside the sea,
  Whose roads lead everywhere to all ;
Than thine no deeper moat can be,
  No steeper fence, no better wall !

Bad news from George on the English throne :
  " You are thriving well," said he ;
" Now by these presents be it known,
  You shall pay us a tax on tea ;
    'T is very small, — no load at all, —
    Honor enough that we send the call."

" Not so," said Boston ; " good my lord,
  We pay your governors here
Abundant for their bed and board,
  Six thousand pounds a year.
(Your highness knows our homely word,)
    Millions for self-government
    But for tribute never a cent."

The cargo came ! and who could blame
  If Indians seized the tea,
And, chest by chest, let down the same
  Into the laughing sea ?
    For what avail the plow or sail,
    Or land or life, if freedom fail ?

The townsmen braved the English king,
  Found friendship in the French,
And Honor joined the patriot ring
  Low on their wooden bench.

O bounteous seas that never fail !
  O day remembered yet !
O happy port that spied the sail
  Which wafted Lafayette !

Pole-star of light in Europe's night,
That never faltered from the right.

Kings shook with fear, old empires crave
  The secret force to find
Which fired the little state to save
  The rights of all mankind.

But right is might through all the world;
  Province to province faithful clung,
Through good and ill the war-bolt hurled,
  Till Freedom cheered and the joy-bells rung.

The sea returning day by day
  Restores the world-wide mart;
So let each dweller on the Bay
  Fold Boston in his heart,
    Till these echoes be choked with snows,
    Or o'er the town blue ocean flows.

Let the blood of her hundred thousands
  Throb in each manly vein;
And the art of all her wisest
  Make sunshine in her brain.
    For you can teach the lightning speech,
    And round the globe your voices reach.

And each shall care for other,
  And each to each shall bend,
To the poor a noble brother,
  To the good an equal friend.

A blessing through the ages thus
  Shield all thy roofs and towers!
God with the fathers, so with us,
  Thou darling town of ours!